Contents

Tick off the che
each topic as you

Section One — Grammar

Section Two — Punctuation

Section Three — Spelling

Section Four — Writers' Techniques

Section Five — Writing

Assessment Tests

Parts of Speech

Clauses

Underline the subordinate clause in each sentence. For example:

Barry stepped back <u>while the parade passed by</u>.

1. The magician looked up when he heard the strange whirring noise.
2. Maria felt nervous after drinking the sickly cough medicine.
3. When the dog had finished gnawing the bone, it chased the cat.
4. The window cleaner ascended the ladder so that he could reach.
5. After the police had departed, there was another unexpected visitor.
6. Sam is combing the gorilla's hair even though it is dangerous.
7. While nobody was looking, Lilijana devoured another biscuit.
8. As soon as we had pitched the tent, we had a well-deserved nap.
9. I will play my trumpet loudly while the neighbours are out.

/ 9

Nouns

Write down whether the word in bold is a proper noun, a collective noun, a common noun or an abstract noun. For example:

The **bunch** of flowers made her feel nostalgic. <u>collective noun</u>

Hint: Have a look at the glossary on p.78 if you're not sure what a technical term means.

10. She will travel from **Germany** for the exhibition. ______________
11. I was pursued through the field by a **herd** of angry cows. ______________
12. It was a bleak, starless night when I returned to the **house**. ______________
13. I appreciate your **honesty** but I can't forgive you. ______________
14. The Pyrenees are a **range** of mountains in Europe. ______________
15. **Hunger** struck Mohammed well before lunch. ______________
16. The netball **team** celebrated its victory. ______________
17. Our greedy dog consumed six sugar-glazed **doughnuts**. ______________
18. Chiyo calmly announced that she was moving to **Bristol**. ______________

/ 9

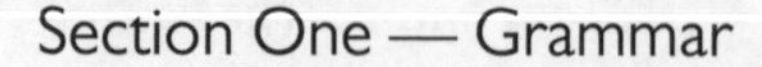

11+ English

For GL Assessment

When it comes to 11+ preparation, nothing beats practice — and this CGP book is packed with the best practice you'll find, all at the perfect level for ages 10-11.

It starts with questions that focus on one topic at a time, so children can really get to grips with each crucial skill. Once they're confident, there's a selection of mixed-topic Assessment Tests to help them get used to the style of the real 11+ papers.

We've also included fully explained answers at the back of the book. Everything you need!

How to access your free Online Edition

This book includes a free Online Edition to read on your PC, Mac or tablet. You'll just need to go to **cgpbooks.co.uk/extras** and enter this code:

4336 2256 7234 7464

By the way, this code only works for one person. If somebody else has used this book before you, they might have already claimed the Online Edition.

Practice Book – Ages 10-11

with Assessment Tests

How to use this Practice Book

This book is divided into two parts — themed question practice and full-length assessment tests. There are answers and detailed explanations at the back of the book.

Themed question practice

- Each page contains practice questions divided by topic. Use these pages to work out your child's strengths and the areas they find tricky. The questions get harder down each page.
- Your child can use the smiley face tick boxes to evaluate how confident they feel with each topic.

Assessment tests

- The second half of the book contains six full-length assessment tests, each with two comprehension texts and a matching set of questions. Each test also includes a set of questions on grammar, spelling and punctuation. They take a similar form to the real test.
- You can print multiple-choice answer sheets so your child can practise the tests as if they're sitting the real thing — visit cgpbooks.co.uk/11plus/answer-sheets or scan the QR code.
- Use the printable answer sheets if you want your child to do each test more than once.
- If you want to give your child timed practice, give them a time limit of 50 minutes for each test, and ask them to work as quickly and carefully as they can.
- The tests get harder from 1-6, so don't be surprised if your child finds the later ones more tricky.
- Your child should aim for a mark of around 85% (43 questions correct) in each test. If they score less than this, use their results to work out the areas they need more practice on.
- If they haven't managed to finish the test in time, they need to work on increasing their speed, whereas if they have made a lot of mistakes, they need to work more carefully.
- Keep track of your child's scores using the progress chart at the back of the book.

Published by CGP

Editors:
Claire Boulter, Heather Gregson, Holly Poynton, Jo Sharrock

Contributors:
Chloe Buckley, Alison Griffin, Steve Martin, Alison Mott, Lucy Towle, Paul Warnes

With thanks to Joe Brazier and Maxine Petrie for the proofreading.

With thanks to Laura Stoney for the copyright research.

ISBN: 978 1 78908 155 8

Printed by Elanders Ltd, Newcastle upon Tyne
Clipart from Corel®

Based on the classic CGP style created by Richard Parsons.

Parts of Speech

Write down whether the word in bold is an adverb, an adjective or a preposition. For example:

The squirrel jumped **over** the fallen tree. preposition

1. The exhausted committee sat **around** the table. ______________
2. Pavel arrived **early** for his initial appointment. ______________
3. Mary was slightly **concerned** when she heard the news. ______________
4. The octopus was a very **talented** pianist. ______________
5. The eagle soared **above** the snow-capped mountains. ______________
6. **Frantically** he searched for the mislaid keys. ______________
7. Although he was poor, he always looked **smart**. ______________
8. The baby wandered unsteadily **through** the door. ______________
9. Anjali contemplated the zip wire **nervously**. ______________

Hint: Adverbs often end with '-ly'.

/ 9

Conjunctions

Underline the most appropriate conjunction from the brackets to complete each sentence. For example:

It has been six years **(when after since)** I saw that film.

10. I reached the crest of the hill **(because before if)** it started raining.
11. Sue would like to train to be a physician **(while when if)** she has left school.
12. Mike gobbled some chips **(unless who while)** Ben was distracted.
13. I adore pasta **(but which if)** I am indifferent towards pizza.
14. The lights have been switched on **(although if because)** it is gloomy.
15. I will make Gran a delicious hot chocolate **(unless if whether)** she would prefer tea.
16. Ned works on Tuesdays **(not whereas until)** Catelyn works on Fridays.
17. Dad had a broken leg **(when and after)** he still went to work.
18. The sun was shining **(so why whereas)** we packed some sun screen.

/ 9

Verbs

Verbs & Subjects

Underline the word or words in each sentence which match the part of speech in brackets. For example:

<u>Paul</u> hurried anxiously down the street. **(subject)**

1. The monk opened the ancient, rusty door. **(subject)**
2. The children giggled at the hamster scuttling about in his cage. **(subject)**
3. Marzia and I viewed the gigantic drifts of snow outside. **(verb)**
4. Khalid and Marcus, the private detectives, resigned. **(verb)**
5. Outside the saloon, the outlaws defied the cruel sheriff. **(verb)**
6. Next summer my family are emigrating to France. **(subject)**
7. Mr Evans sighed as he gave Aleksandra's sister a new book. **(subject)**
8. Singing hurts my sore throat. **(subject)**
9. After a heavy snow fall, Sally's mum abandoned the car. **(verb)**

Hint: The subject is usually followed by a verb.

/ 9

Verbs

Write down whether each sentence is active or passive. For example:

Chris threw the ball through the window. ___active___

10. Jean generously invited everyone to her house for refreshments. ________
11. The solo performer was a precocious young girl with talent. ________
12. Abdul, with outstretched hands, caught the rabbit as it fell. ________
13. The driver was prevented from going any further by the police. ________
14. Kate screamed as she heard the scrape of the lock behind her. ________
15. The prizes were presented by the new head teacher. ________
16. I will be given a new set of false teeth for my birthday. ________
17. The door was flung open by a woman with yellow shoes. ________
18. The charities expect to reach their fundraising target by May. ________

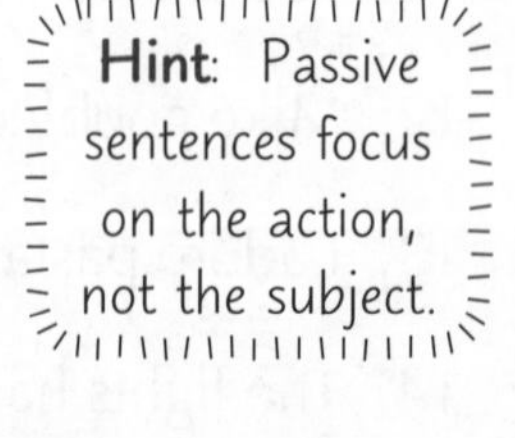

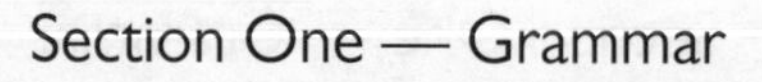

Verbs

Verbs

Underline the correct verb from the brackets to complete each sentence. For example:

I **(is be am)** taking extra science classes.

1. When the hurricane was over, the boat **(sink sank sinks)** to the sea floor.
2. I **(were was am)** suffering last week, but I have improved since then.
3. **(Write Wrote Writing)** clearly so people can comprehend what you mean.
4. Leo reached the door, timidly raised his hand and **(rang rung ring)** the bell.
5. It's important that she **(continue continuing continued)** to learn Spanish in the future.
6. I **(have am had)** just finished my dinner when I heard the shrill scream.
7. If I **(will would were)** to win the prize, I would buy a new car.
8. The gerbil had **(forgot forget forgotten)** where its tail was.
9. This morning I **(is am will)** be going to work in a spaceship.

/ 9

Verbs

Complete each sentence using the correct form of the verb in brackets. Write your answer on the line. For example:

The rotten piece of cheese was stolen **(to steal)** by the mouse.

10. I ___________ **(to speak)** in class, so the teacher shouted at me.
11. Pedro had never ___________ **(to lend)** me his favourite CD.
12. Who were you ___________ **(to visit)** yesterday?
13. Vivienne says she will go to the zoo if Edwina ___________ **(to come)** too.
14. Last month I ___________ **(to do)** an hour of exercise every day.
15. We were on our way to Wales when we ___________ **(to notice)** the deflated tyre.
16. When the boat capsized, the sailor ___________ **(to swim)** back to shore.
17. Mr Thomas ___________ **(to throw)** his socks in the washing machine yesterday.
18. He ___________ **(to bring)** crisps and lemonade to last summer's picnic.

Hint: Make sure the verb agrees with the subject and check that the tenses in each sentence agree.

/ 9

Mixed Grammar Questions

Each sentence has one grammatical error. Underline the word which is wrong and write the correct word on the line. For example:

Sarah and Kevin <u>is</u> getting married in June. are

1. We must apologise because Louise ate all theirs lollipops. ______
2. I were going to tell you the story when I arrived. ______
3. The discontented children have wrote a long letter to their MP. ______
4. The rusty car was advancing very slow towards the main road. ______
5. I saw the cricketer throws the ball into the river. ______
6. That ornamental rocking horse used to be my. ______
7. What of these crayons shall I use for this drawing? ______
8. We don't want no unnecessary noise from you. ______
9. There is no available seats on this rickety bus. ______

/ 9

Underline the word in each sentence which matches the part of speech in brackets. For example:

Kieran <u>cleared</u> the table in a hurry. **(verb)**

10. Charlotte goes to school in the centre of the city. **(proper noun)**
11. The fire was lit swiftly and the room felt warmer. **(adjective)**
12. The teacher tossed the work back to her disdainfully. **(pronoun)**
13. The grey elephant sighed regretfully in the circus van. **(adverb)**
14. In the swimming pool, the children played contentedly. **(verb)**
15. Alice hurried nervously after the mouse. **(common noun)**
16. The girl took the penultimate train to Edinburgh. **(preposition)**
17. The canary-yellow car drew up alongside the shops. **(adjective)**
18. The thief probably hid the stolen jewels under his mattress. **(adverb)**

Hint: A proper noun starts with a capital letter and names things like people and places.

/ 9

Mixed Grammar Questions

Underline the most appropriate word from the brackets to complete each sentence. For example:

Jonathan **(is am be are)** going to the match tomorrow.

Hint: Say the sentence out loud to help you work out the missing word.

1. I am not allowed out **(although when because why)** I returned home late last night.
2. Rob was playing the **(worse worst awful badly)** game of rugby of his whole career.
3. The baby **(waked wakes woke woken)** up early and was gurgling quietly.
4. Dan ran ten miles **(because despite yet thus)** the very high temperature.
5. She had **(spoke spoken speak told)** to them about road safety.
6. We told him that the football stickers were **(our ours we us)**.

/ 6

7. Greta and her cousin **(likes likely enjoy like)** to go cycling in all conditions.
8. As he **(shake shook shaken shaked)** the groundsheet, a tiny spider sprang out.
9. **(Although Yet But Where)** the man was in agony, he limped to the hospital.
10. Raj **(cut cuts cutted cutting)** his glossy, curly hair when his mother was distracted.
11. There is a warning for all drivers to drive **(safe careful carefully quick)**.
12. I discovered the pencil **(what when which where)** I had mislaid.

/ 6

13. I would like to introduce you to my friend who **(going gone went go)** to Norway.
14. **(Therefore When But Moreover)** the puppy could not go outside, it became quite lethargic.
15. Davinda did not admit that she solved all of the equations **(easy easiest easily easiness)**.
16. Angus realised that he **(had has have is)** broken his mother's priceless vase.
17. The polar bear **(taken take takes took)** an indirect route yesterday.
18. I enjoy eating trifle **(since whereas besides despite)** Rebecca likes apple pie.

Commas and Brackets

Brackets

Each of these sentences is missing a pair of brackets. Add brackets around the correct words in each sentence. For example:

Mr Smith (my neighbour) was mowing his lawn.

1. The M.P. Member of Parliament gave a rousing speech .
2. I despise vegetables especially carrots .
3. I'm catching a long-haul flight this evening Friday .
4. It costs £185 per child 7-11 years .
5. Sprint a verb means to run quickly .
6. I saw Miss Chaudhary my tutor shopping today .
7. Our vehicle is red bright red with a turquoise stripe .
8. Eclairs buns filled with cream are mouth-watering treats .
9. The pencils which belong to class 4 have been lost .

Hint: Remember that brackets are used to add extra information or explanations.

/ 9

Commas

Add one comma to each sentence so that it is correct. For example:

The door, which was bright red, shone in the sunlight.

10. Trembling with anticipation she opened the door.
11. The fox hesitated glared and sauntered away.
12. Mrs Jones, 46 witnessed the dangerous incident.
13. I sold my holiday cottage and moved to Maidstone Kent.
14. The panda just 3 months old, was absolutely adorable.
15. Evania Aunt Kirsty and Gita are intrepid mountaineers.
16. Before leaving the bandits, fearsome and imposing, put on their masks.
17. The goalkeeper, my best friend played superbly.
18. So, if you feel inspired start writing your own blog.

Dashes and Hyphens

Dashes

Add a single dash or a pair of dashes to each sentence so that it is correct. For example:

Humayra — the newest student in school — was late for class.

1. It was no use the lock wouldn't open without the correct key.
2. The acrobats the most popular act at the circus didn't perform last night.
3. She saw the manager Betsey walking to the carpark.
4. The town was deserted there was nobody in sight.
5. Flopsy gobbled up the pieces of carrot they were delicious.
6. To reach the tallest waterfall which was 200m high we walked for hours.
7. I went straight home there was nothing I could do to help.
8. My eldest brother who had always loved art painted me a picture.
9. I didn't know where to go he wouldn't tell me.

/ 9

Hyphens

Write down whether each sentence uses hyphens correctly or incorrectly. For example:

I took the wooden-handled bag to the supermarket. correct

10. The long-legged bird waded through the murky water. ______________
11. I found a half eaten-apple under the table. ______________
12. The teacher took the seven-year old children to the library. ______________
13. Are you sure this is the most up-to-date model? ______________
14. It was midnight before the wind and heavy-rain stopped. ______________
15. The dog stole the plate of warm-fresh cookies. ______________
16. The athletes have trained hard for this month-long event. ______________
17. There were twelve-sky-high-trees in the palace gardens. ______________
18. I won't go-you should carry on without me. ______________

/ 9

Apostrophes

Apostrophes

One word in each sentence is missing an apostrophe. Underline the word and write out the correct version on the line. For example:

My parents car is old and rusty ___parents'___

1. Novak wasnt allowed to play chess. ______________
2. The tigers paw was tangled in some yarn. ______________
3. We think shell win all the trophies. ______________
4. Mr Smiths hat blew away in the breeze. ______________
5. Wed like a chocolate-covered cookie. ______________
6. The babies rattles were grubby. ______________
7. Were a disgruntled group of people. ______________
8. The womens handbags were spacious. ______________
9. Both the bikes wheels had fallen off. ______________

Hint: Look for words that show possession as well as shortened versions of words.

/ 9

Apostrophes

Use either **it's** or **its** to complete each sentence. For example:

John's scooter fell onto ___its___ side.

10. __________ snowing outside; the flakes are tumbling down like feathers.
11. The dog licked __________ paw after the inconsiderate owner stood on it.
12. "__________ been ages since we met!" she gasped excitedly.
13. I think __________ time to go as everyone seems weary.
14. Italy is famous for __________ delicious cuisine.
15. Sometimes __________ hard to apologise, especially when you don't feel remorse.
16. I swerved out of the way as the car flashed __________ lights at me.
17. I hate my uncontrollable frizzy hair, so __________ time for a change!
18. The shop helpfully opened __________ doors early for us.

/ 9

Inverted Commas, Colons and Semicolons

Inverted Commas

Rewrite this reported speech as direct speech. For example:

Oliver told his mum that he had eaten the cake.
"I have eaten the cake," Oliver told his mum.

1. She said that the toffees were delicious.

____

2. Pasua claimed that she was on time last night.

____

3. He asked politely if he could be excused.

____

4. Carlos explained that it wasn't his fault.

____

5. He admitted that he started the fire.

____

/ 5

Colons & Semicolons

Add a colon or a semicolon to complete each sentence. For example:

They were missing three important things**:** a bucket, a spade and a ball.

6. There are some items you need to bring a towel, sunglasses and some goggles.
7. The shop sold mints as big as fists sweets that fizzed; and dark liquorice balls.
8. Roberto knew what was about to happen he was going to be sick.
9. The referee sent the footballer off Liang visibly winced as he passed.
10. Julie had visited several countries Turkey, Thailand and Brazil.
11. Cheese gives me nightmares I don't eat it before bedtime.
12. The girl was motivated by one thing her love of money.
13. There are five vowels in the alphabet a, e, i, o and u.
14. Fiona's book was very interesting she couldn't stop reading it.

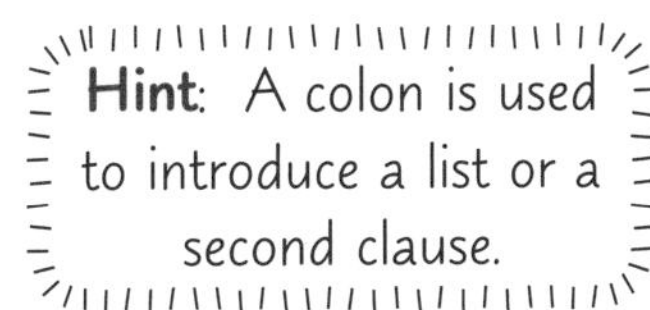

Mixed Punctuation Questions

Each of these sentences contains one punctuation error. Underline the word with the mistake and write the correct version on the line. For example:

The clown didnt really like children. didn't

1. The sea is at it's most rough during the winter months. ____________
2. The actress paused at the thought of going to spain. ____________
3. "It is only a puppet," The comedian said brightly. ____________
4. "Who want's cake?" Rashad enquired, waving a spoon. ____________
5. The dogs slobbered hungrily all over the mens shoes. ____________
6. Balding Men often choose to shave their heads. ____________
7. "I could'nt wait to leave the city," whispered Brian. ____________
8. Bronagh bought some ingredients: Eggs, flour, milk and sugar. ____________
9. I'm unable to go to Yosefs birthday party in two days' time. ____________

/ 9

Each of these sentences is missing one punctuation mark. Add the missing punctuation mark to each of the sentences. For example:

Where did you go ?

10. " Don't pop the balloon ! Melissa shouted frantically .
11. " Have those bikes been abandoned " asked the policeman .
12. The sun , which was nearly setting shone in the driver's eyes .
13. Skateboarding is something that children and some adults) are good at .
14. " Make sure your experiment is precise " the professor instructed .
15. Mario smiled with satisfaction the room was spotlessly clean .
16. You need three items of stationery a pen , a pencil case and a notepad .
17. The latest fashions in a variety of styles and sizes , are on sale now .
18. The lorries number plates were covered in grime and dust .

Mixed Punctuation Questions

These short passages have no punctuation. Rewrite the passages with the correct punctuation. Each passage has 10 missing punctuation marks.

1. buster was beaming at him and although he was angry the boy found himself reluctant to shout at the puppy with his glossy fur wet little nose and floppy ears you are so troublesome he muttered

____

/ 10

2. buttons played by joe greco was the star of the pantomime all the critics agreed that the scenery and lighting could not have been better what a success

____

/ 10

3. my birthday party is being held at carnwick village hall theres going to be a clown and a chocolate gateau it will be the best ever

____

/ 10

Plurals

Plurals

Write the correct plural of the word in brackets. For example:

The choir performed in several churches **(church)**.

1. Gita was a scientist who studied sediments and ______________ **(volcano)**.
2. There are no ______________ **(wolf)** living wild in England now.
3. The tribe has had three different ______________ **(chief)** in the last decade.
4. The local people campaigned to keep the county's ______________ **(library)** open.
5. The removal man sighed as he saw the ______________ **(piano)** he had to move.
6. Felicity detested eating ______________ **(tomato)**, even on pizza!
7. The clumsy ______________ **(thief)** were destined to get caught.
8. Santa's ______________ **(elf)** were back in the workshop on Boxing Day.
9. Snow covered the ______________ **(roof)** of the houses opposite.

/ 9

Plurals

Write the correct plural of the word in brackets. For example:

The cook put cheese in traps to catch the mice **(mouse)**.

10. We stopped at several tropical ______________ **(oasis)** on our walk.
11. Sunita learnt how to identify edible ______________ **(fungus)**.
12. I want to purchase ______________ **(this)** football boots.
13. Fillipe and Jasmine played a game that involved rolling several ______________ **(die)**.
14. Cerys went to the park very early in the morning to watch the ______________ **(deer)**.
15. There's me, my mum and my sisters, so my dad is surrounded by ______________ **(woman)**.
16. When my brother cooked dinner, it was a long series of ______________ **(crisis)**.
17. "Hand over ______________ **(that)** custard pies at once!" my mum said angrily.
18. Many ______________ **(moose)** were grazing peacefully on the plain.

Hint: These words are irregular so sometimes letters in the middle of the word will change.

/ 9

Homophones

Homophones

Choose the correct homophone from the brackets. For example:

Archie tied a strong __knot__ **(knot not)** in the ship's rigging.

1. The farmer had to move his stubborn ___________ **(heard herd)** of cows into the barn.
2. Tanay didn't know ___________ **(whether weather)** to eat the chocolate cake or the jelly.
3. It's vital to have a good breakfast; eating a nutritious ___________ **(cereal serial)** can help.
4. Rebecca flexed the strong ___________ **(muscles mussels)** in her arms.
5. The tomato ___________ **(source sauce)** was as thick as treacle.
6. The ice-cream van drove ___________ **(past passed)** the waiting crowd.
7. The wild wind blew the weather ___________ **(vain vane)** off the church roof.
8. The ___________ **(soul sole)** of my shoe had a gaping hole in it.
9. Queen Victoria ___________ **(reigned reined)** for 63 years.

/9

Homophones

Underline the correct homophone to complete the sentence.
For example:

The ticket will be in **(yore you're <u>your</u>)** wallet.

10. The boomerang landed in the shrubs over **(they're their there)**.
11. If it's not **(to two too)** late, I'm going to come to the theatre.
12. Mika wanted to **(by buy bye)** a Christmas gift for his colleague.
13. Amy didn't have the faintest clue **(wear where ware)** she was going.
14. This wasn't the **(write rite right)** time to mention that the test had been postponed.
15. Asif was in **(ore oar awe)** of his older brother's new motorbike.
16. There was a long **(pours paws pause)** as an awkward silence filled the room.
17. **(By Buy Bye)** now for the lowest prices and best deals in town!
18. Vicky was given a lot of **(prays preys praise)** for her volunteer work.

Prefixes and Suffixes

Prefixes

Choose the correct prefix from the list to complete the word in each sentence: **un**, **in**, **pre**, **mis**, **re** or **dis**. For example:

Marcie felt very __un__lucky because she never won anything.

1. I thought she was a coward, but I was _______taken.
2. The detective was _______certain that the suspect was guilty.
3. Mum's carrot cake was simply _______edible!
4. Go back the way you came to _______trace your steps.
5. It would be _______honest to say he had left the homework on the bus.
6. There have been many positive _______views of the new film.
7. Mrs Sajedi was _______capable of being bad-tempered around the children.
8. The burly men inside the car were obviously having a _______agreement.
9. Make sure you _______heat the oven to the right temperature before you start.

Hint: Remember that 'pre' means 'before' and 're' means 'again'.

/ 9

Suffixes

Complete these sentences by adding a suffix to the word in brackets. For example:

That was such a __thoughtful__ **(thought)** present.

10. The _______________ **(music)** took a deep breath as he took to the stage with his guitar.
11. The sergeant demands loyalty, hard work and _______________ **(tidy)** from her soldiers.
12. I have fond memories from my _______________ **(child)** when I lived in the countryside.
13. Stacey wanted to avoid getting into an _______________ **(argue)** about the missing book.
14. Many children around the world don't receive any _______________ **(educate)**.
15. Daneesh was very _______________ **(hope)** that they would find his gerbil, Patches.
16. My brother has an _______________ **(imagine)** friend called Brutas.
17. The stolen jewellery was precious and very _______________ **(value)**.
18. The elderly skydiver was a very _______________ **(courage)** man.

/ 9

Awkward Spellings

Vowels

Add either **ie** or **ei** to form the words correctly. For example:

Jamie had a br_ie_f wait at the station before his train arrived.

1. Abdul stood nervously on the stage as he waited to rec_____ve his prize.
2. The baubles dangling from the c_____ling were glittering in the lamp light.
3. Isabelle dec_____ved her dad by pretending to have done her homework.
4. When the spaceship landed in the garden, Peter knew he was having a w_____rd day.
5. The businessman used the newspaper to sh_____ld himself from the rain.
6. Frankie could perc_____ve the distant sound of an ice cream van.
7. My dad and my brother are both interested in books set in med_____val times.
8. Mrs DiFranco loves knitting and going swimming at the l_____sure centre.
9. The police officer s_____zed the man by the arm and marched him to the exit.

/ 9

Consonants

Complete these words with the correct pair of consonants so that the sentence makes sense. For example:

The cli_ff_s by the sea looked very difficult to cli_mb_.

Hint: Each letter pair is either a pair of double letters or has one silent letter.

10. Mina caught her thu_____ in the blades of the _____issors.
11. The chef cho_____ed the cabbage with a sharp _____ife.
12. The kitten's fur, which used to be flu_____y, was dri_____ing wet.
13. Grandma was busy _____itting a jumper for her li_____le grandson.
14. The hotel's acco_____odation was very expensive, so they ignored the vacancy si_____.
15. Jimmy asked his mother if she would _____ite a note to excuse him from going swi_____ing.
16. When he jumped into the pu_____le, the water came up to his _____ees!
17. The rabbit's flo_____y ears dangled as he ni_____led on a carrot.
18. The dashing _____ight picked up his helmet and _____ord before the battle.

/ 9

Mixed Spelling Questions

Each sentence contains a spelling mistake. Underline the word with the error and write the correct spelling on the line. For example:

Only three contestants remaned in the competition. remained

1. The children were extreamly anxious about their voyage. ________
2. Wolfgang strolled glumly along the corridor, feeling embarased. ________
3. It was the forth time this week that James had missed a deadline. ________
4. Marsha didn't enjoy going on long distence walks in the country. ________
5. Simone knew that her football team were definately going to succeed. ________
6. Mum's casserole was discusting; she wasn't the world's best chef. ________

Hint: Once you've identified the error, remember to write the correct spelling on the line.

/ 6

7. Joe stuck on his fake moustache; it was the final piece of his disgise. ________
8. Gustav tried to convinse the teacher not to give him detention. ________
9. My stomack aches because I've eaten far too much lasagne. ________
10. The coach blew his whistle and expected an imediate response. ________
11. The crowd erupted into applause, which deafend the actors on stage. ________
12. Amy was alarmed by the shriek and glanced behind her hesitently. ________

/ 6

13. The letters were privite, but Adam could not resist reading them. ________
14. Once the seleccion box was opened, Sam rushed to grab a biscuit. ________
15. Anya was desparate to win this year's school talent competition. ________
16. I paid for my taxi but the driver was reluctant to give me a reciept. ________
17. It was ridiculous how much the restaurant charged for desert. ________
18. Gakuya arrived at the concert early so she was garanteed a seat. ________

/ 6

Mixed Spelling Questions

Underline the correct word to complete each sentence. For example:

The pens are in the **(stationary <u>stationery</u>)** cupboard.

1. Faizah likes to **(practise practice)** the piano every Wednesday afternoon.
2. Skateboarding is a skill that takes a lot of **(practise practice)**.

3. Closing the local shop will have a negative **(effect affect)** on the village.
4. Numerous factors can **(affect effect)** global climate change.

5. In America, a head teacher is called a **(principle principal)**.
6. Bijan turned down the job on **(principle principal)**.

7. There are **(less fewer)** ducks on the pond than there were yesterday.
8. I have a lot **(less fewer)** money now that I've been on holiday.

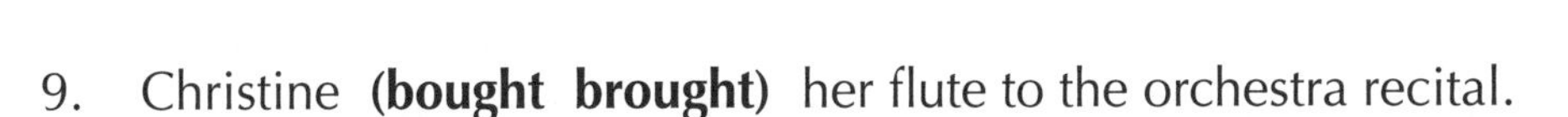

9. Christine **(bought brought)** her flute to the orchestra recital.
10. Keisha **(bought brought)** the last pineapple in the entire market.

11. I was delighted when my sister **(past passed)** her driving test.
12. During the **(past passed)** year, I've saved enough money to buy a new camera.

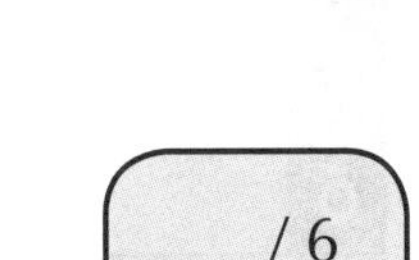

13. Agony Aunts often give their readers **(advice advise)** on relationships.
14. I would **(advice advise)** you to take off your socks before you paddle in the sea.

15. We **(accept except)** your apology, but please don't wake us up so early again.
16. Brianne adores all animals **(accept except)** snakes and lizards.

17. Professor Tate is trying to **(device devise)** a way of travelling through time.
18. My mobile phone is the only **(device devise)** I can't live without.

Alliteration and Onomatopoeia

Alliteration

Underline all of the words that form the alliteration. For example:

The <u>baby</u> <u>beamed</u> at the <u>big</u> <u>blue</u> <u>balloon</u>.

1. The giant jumped as the giraffe's jaws grasped the branches.
2. Zehira fanned the flames furiously as she fought to phone the firemen.
3. The king crept behind the dusty curtains, which caused him to choke.
4. The pony pranced while the phantom played a prank.
5. Hannah hoped that Henry would not be home an hour late.
6. Veronika knew that she had nearly knocked over the new fence.
7. Wendy watched the writers while they tried on wacky wigs.
8. The gnome graciously guarded the grand and glorious garden.
9. The robber raided the wrong room before he was wrestled to the ground.

Hint: Look out for the same sounds at the beginning of words, not just the same letter.

/ 9

Onomatopoeia

Underline the onomatopoeic word in each sentence. For example:

The sausages were slowly <u>sizzling</u> in the pan as I threw the egg away.

10. Veronica screamed in fright when the leaves began to rustle.
11. Hissing, the wild cat spun around to inspect its quivering prey.
12. The door banged shut as Achmed stormed out of the room.
13. Fatima heard her brother's wheezing cough echo through the house.
14. I cheered loudly and my friend tooted the horn as his car's engine burst into life.
15. The bicycle whizzed past Stephanie at top speed.
16. The lemonade fizzed gently as Sam poured it into the guests' glasses.
17. I yelped when my brother stood on my toe — it made my foot tingle.
18. The boy loved to sit by the crackling fire and watch the flames leap over the logs.

Hint: Look for words that imitate the sound of the action or object.

/ 9

Imagery

Imagery

Each sentence contains a metaphor, a simile or personification. Write down which technique is being used for each sentence. For example:

Susan was a monkey as she clambered up the tree. metaphor

Hint: Similes often use the words 'like' or 'as'.

1. The sun smiled down on the holiday-makers basking below. ____________
2. His teacher was a bitter woman; she had a heart of pure ice. ____________
3. Jaione's grandfather was a wise, old owl perched in his chair. ____________
4. The newspapers' headlines screamed, "Robbery!" ____________
5. The angry man stomped across the room like an elephant. ____________
6. The footballer was a streak of lightning as he raced to the goal. ____________
7. The moonlight danced on the waves, causing the spray to shimmer. ____________
8. The snow was a soft, white blanket covering the town. ____________
9. The Christmas lights were as bright as diamonds. ____________

/ 9

Imagery

Complete these similes and metaphors using a suitable word or phrase. For example:

The lorry was as slow as a snail.

Hint: Use your imagination for these questions but make sure that what you write makes sense.

10. The hot room was a ____________________.
11. Her face was as red as a ____________________.
12. The graceful dancer was a ____________________.
13. His father shouted as loudly as a ____________________.
14. Mrs Brown ran along the road like a ____________________.
15. His knowledge was as valuable as ____________________.
16. The soldier moved as quickly as a ____________________.
17. The forest was as dark as ____________________.
18. Her tall uncle was a ____________________.

/ 9

Abbreviations

Abbreviations

Write down the full word for the abbreviation in bold. For example:

Sgt Watson yelled commands at the soldiers. Sergeant

1. The weight of the car was **approx** 1 tonne. ________
2. His coat had been handed in to the Lost Property **Dept**. ________
3. Veronique had grown 7 **cm** in the last year. ________
4. The fresh, juicy apple only cost 60**p**. ________
5. Today's match is Grizebeck Wanderers **v** Antieul Villa. ________
6. Her address was 4 Ivy **Ave**, Teddington, Bumbleshire. ________
7. **Prof** Swine was a famous scientist. ________
8. He climbed to the very top of **Mt** Lion. ________
9. The recipe needs 12 **oz** of softened unsalted butter. ________

/ 9

Write down whether the word in bold is an acronym or an abbreviated word. For example:

My aunt Michaela works for the **BBC**. acronym

Hint: Remember that the letters in acronyms stand for words and are usually in upper case.

10. Julia's mother worked for WorkWear **Ltd**. ________
11. I am fascinated by stars, planets and **NASA**. ________
12. I am a life-long supporter of Ulverston **Utd**. ________
13. Marcus Richardson **Jr** would inherit the company. ________
14. The **max** temperature recorded was 34 °C. ________
15. **FIFA** funded the construction of a new football stadium. ________
16. Arnd buys his clothes from the Ethical Clothing **Co**. ________
17. Holidays in **Aug** will not be authorised. ________
18. France is a member of **NATO**. ________

/ 9

Synonyms and Antonyms

Synonyms

Underline the word from the brackets that is the best synonym for the word in bold. For example:

The river was **broad**. **(flowing muddy wide)**

1. The **ruined** castle was seven miles from his house. **(shabby antique derelict)**
2. Ben was **apprehensive** about performing in the concert. **(suspicious unaware anxious)**
3. Polly **comforted** her friend after he lost the tournament. **(consoled assisted criticised)**
4. The boy was **scolded** for eating the whole cake. **(blamed banished teased)**
5. Hiro's grandfather was as **amusing** as ever. **(talkative entertaining kind)**
6. The motor would no longer **rotate**. **(function revolve move)**
7. Robina felt **intimidated** by the exam. **(daunted astonished outraged)**
8. They made the **hazardous** journey over the mountain. **(cautious lengthy dangerous)**
9. Rebecca was **chased** by a big black dog. **(pursued assaulted joined)**

Hint: Synonyms are words which mean the same thing.

/ 9

Antonyms

Underline the word from the brackets that is the best antonym for the word in bold. For example:

Peter found the visit **dull**. **(exciting dreary upsetting)**

10. Nigel **loathed** spaghetti because it looked like worms. **(preferred relished devoured)**
11. The film's ending was quite **bewildering**. **(shocking clear serious)**
12. The river continued its **sluggish** journey to the sea. **(long direct rapid)**
13. Jennifer was **aware** of the hysteria in the air. **(ignorant uninterested informed)**
14. The explorer's companions **hindered** her progress. **(helped delayed checked)**
15. Mehtab's new haircut made her feel **confident**. **(unsure quiet short)**
16. Jean-Marc was **appalled** by the state of his flat. **(impressed embarrassed fascinated)**
17. The goats were **sheltered** on the cliff face. **(precarious endangered exposed)**
18. Her welcoming speech seemed **genuine**. **(invalid flawed insincere)**

Hint: Antonym means 'opposite meaning'.

Spotting and Understanding Devices

Read the passage below, then answer the questions that follow.

The dreary drops of rain drizzled down. Tom splashed through the puddles and dodged the spray from the cars that whizzed past. His smile was the only sunlight in the grey day. The smile quickly faded, however, as uninvited doubts began to go through his mind.

"What if they don't let me go on the school trip to the sci-fi film festival? What if Mum
5 won't sign the form? What if Mr Green has filled all the places?"

"Hey, Tom!" Tom looked up to see his friend Wenona waving at him from the other side of the street. She looked like a slender elf with her big ears sticking out from beneath her hat. Tom was about to reply when a huge lorry screamed past and launched a wave of water over him
10 before racing away. Tom was drenched!

Hint: The techniques in the passage will only be things that have been covered in this section.

Write down which technique is used in the following:

1. "The dreary drops of rain drizzled down" (line 1) ______________
2. "Tom splashed through the puddles" (line 1) ______________
3. "His smile was the only sunlight" (line 2) ______________
4. "She looked like a slender elf" (line 7) ______________

Write down an example from the text of the following:

5. an abbreviation ______________________________
6. personification ______________________________
7. a synonym of 'bleak' ______________
8. an antonym of 'dry' ______________
9. an antonym of 'broad' ______________
10. a synonym of 'rapidly' ______________

/ 10

Spotting and Understanding Devices

Read the passage below, then answer the questions that follow.
Underline the correct option for each question.

"You've missed again," the soldier muttered, as the grappling hook just missed its target. As he heard the angry shouts in the distance, he was reminded just how important this mission was. He looked up at the cruel watchtower nearby.

"Well, I'll just have to try again, won't I?" the other man said, as he took aim once more.
5 "After all, everyone knows that that's where the prisoner is being held. All I have to do is climb over that 10-mile high wall, overpower a few hundred guards, break through a steel door and rescue him. Easy!"

The second grappling hook shot through the dark night sky like a rocket and clanged against the top of the wall.
10 "Who's there?" The snarling voice was a dagger ripping through the silence of the night.

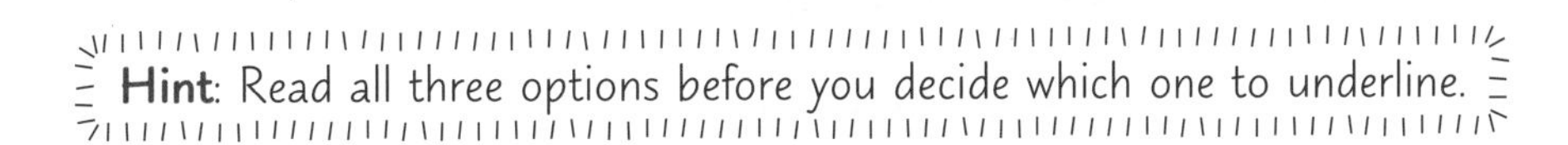

1. The author says that the soldier "muttered" (line 1).
   What impression does this give you of the soldier?

   A He's annoyed. **B** He's tired. **C** He's shy.

2. The author compares the grappling hook to a "rocket" (line 9). What does this tell you about the grappling hook?

   A It is dangerous. **B** It moves quickly. **C** It makes a banging noise.

3. The hook "clanged" (line 9) against the wall. What effect does this word have on the reader?

   A It shocks the reader. **B** It makes the story scary. **C** It helps you imagine the noise.

4. The voice is described as a "dagger" (line 10). This shows that the speaker is:

   A dangerous. **B** strong. **C** brave.

5. The man says that he needs to climb over "that 10-mile wall" (line 6). Why does he say this?

   A He's exaggerating. **B** He's intimidated. **C** He can't see very well.

6. Why does the man say that overpowering the guards will be "Easy" (line 7)?

   A He's being practical. **B** He's being optimistic. **C** He's being ironic.

Writing Fiction

Adjectives

You can improve your writing by using a variety of adjectives. Replace the word in bold with a different adjective which has the same meaning. For example:

He opened the **old** book. ancient

1. The thief was a **bad** man. ________
2. The **cold** wind made him shiver. ________
3. Mei wished she had not watched the **scary** film. ________
4. The tourists took pictures of the **pretty** view. ________
5. Nishi had never seen such an **angry** teacher. ________
6. They all had a **nice** day at the zoo. ________
7. The orange-flavoured crisps tasted a bit **strange**. ________
8. The new team member was an **amazing** player. ________
9. The class were **noisy** as they waited for the teacher. ________

Hint: Use a thesaurus to help you find suitable adjectives.

/ 9

Clauses

Add a clause to complete these sentences. Make sure your writing is exciting and interesting. For example:

He opened the door, hoping the beast was not waiting for him.

10. Muniza went to school ________
11. Tia ate her dinner ________
12. Mr Greg smiled ________
13. He jumped into the pool ________
14. Franziska looked at her bike ________
15. The boy cried ________
16. The netball team lost ________
17. Fiona listened to the singing ________
18. He walked over the bridge ________

/ 9

Writing Fiction

Adjectives

Adjectives make your stories more detailed and interesting.
Write three adjectives to describe these characters, settings and events.
For example:

A pirate ___cruel___ ___seasick___ ___unfriendly___

Hint: Use your imagination to picture what each of these is like.

1. A dragon ______ ______ ______
2. An island ______ ______ ______
3. A car chase ______ ______ ______
4. A cave ______ ______ ______
5. A wizard ______ ______ ______
6. A graveyard ______ ______ ______

/ 6

7. A competition ______ ______ ______
8. A party ______ ______ ______
9. A granny ______ ______ ______
10. A hut ______ ______ ______
11. A boat journey ______ ______ ______
12. A pilot ______ ______ ______

/ 6

Write a plan for each of these titles, then turn your plan into a story.
Try to write about 500 words for each.

Hint: Be original — if you get a question about a dream holiday, a story about a trip to an unusual place will grab the reader's attention.

13. Write a story with the title "My Dream Holiday".
14. Write a story with the title "My Greatest Achievement".
15. Write a story with the title "The Mysterious Locked Door".
16. Write a story with the title "Lost in the Jungle".
17. Write a story that starts with the sentence "I was lying in bed, trying to drift off to sleep, when it hit me like a bolt of lightning; I knew what I needed to do to make the invention work."

Writing Non-Fiction

You can improve your own writing by understanding the purpose of different texts. Write down whether each sentence is describing (D), persuading (P) or informing (I). For example:

The Tudors were English monarchs. I

1. This summer, visit Yardby, where there's lots to do and great beaches. ____
2. The penguin's sleek feathers glistened in the morning sun. ____
3. Donate to 'Cats in Hats' and keep a poor kitten warm this winter. ____
4. Badminton is a sport played with a racket and a shuttlecock. ____
5. Mount Everest is the highest mountain in the world at over 29 000 ft. ____
6. The day was crisp and bright, with gleaming frost glazing the grass. ____
7. Please don't throw litter into my garden; I'm 72 and it hurts to pick it up. ____

/ 7

Write a plan for these essays. Include a point for the introduction, three points for the middle and a point for your conclusion.

Hint: Take one side of the argument and try to persuade the reader to agree with you.

8. **It's better to live in the countryside than in the city. Do you agree?**

Intro: ____

Middle 1: ____

2: ____

3: ____

Conclusion: ____

/ 5

9. **Should mobile phones be banned in schools?**

Intro: ____

Middle 1: ____

2: ____

3: ____

Conclusion: ____

/ 5

Writing Non-Fiction

Write a sentence arguing **for** and **against** these statements.
For example:

People should visit more countries.
For: It's important to learn about other cultures.
Against: Long flights are bad for the environment.

1. **All children should wear school uniform.**
   For: ________________
   Against: ________________ / 2

2. **People should cycle instead of driving.**
   For: ________________
   Against: ________________ / 2

3. **Everyone should own a pet.**
   For: ________________
   Against: ________________ / 2

4. **Children should watch more television.**
   For: ________________
   Against: ________________ / 2

5. **Being fashionable is important.**
   For: ________________
   Against: ________________ / 2

Write a plan for each of these titles, then turn your plan into a full answer. Try to write about 500 words for each.

6. Write a letter to your aunt persuading her to let you visit her on her tropical island.
7. Write an article for the school newsletter informing people about a club or hobby.
8. All children should play a musical instrument. Do you agree?
9. Write an essay about the person you admire the most.
10. Write an essay describing your perfect birthday party.

Hint: Make sure that you know how to start and end letters correctly.

Assessment Test 1

The rest of this book contains six assessment tests, which get progressively harder. Allow 50 minutes to do each test and work as quickly and as carefully as you can.

If you want to attempt each test more than once, you will need to print **multiple-choice answer sheets** for these questions from our website — go to cgpbooks.co.uk/11plus/answer-sheets or scan the QR code on the right. If you'd prefer to answer the questions on the page, just follow the instructions in the question.

Read this passage carefully and answer the questions that follow.

The First Day

Daniel felt as if he was being swallowed alive as he walked down the rowdy corridor and squinted through the thick lenses of his spectacles at the school hall beyond. The corridor was like the throat of a terrifying beast and he was sliding down it into the big belly that was the school hall.

He knew what would happen when he got there. All the new pupils, like himself, would be sitting
5 in rows waiting for the headmaster to make his welcome address. The headmaster at St. Joseph's was a towering, severe man who could strike fear into any pupil. He was not a man who would put up with any nonsense whatsoever. Daniel knew this. He knew it because when Mr Graham was not busy being the headmaster, he was busy being Daniel's dad. Now, of course, his dad would be able to do both simultaneously and Daniel was sure that he would be teased for it. He felt thoroughly miserable; he was
10 never going to make any friends.

"Hello," a voice said behind him. "You must be new too. My name's Rachael."

The girl was stunning. She thrust her hand out confidently towards Daniel, while he gaped at her.

"Dennis!" he blurted, finally shaking her hand, "I mean... Daniel. My name's Daniel."

"Don't you know your own name?" Rachael laughed. She didn't seem to be nervous at all.

15 "You're the head teacher's son, aren't you? Everyone says he's intimidating but my brother Tom (who's in the year above us) says that his bark is worse than his bite. It'll be weird for you, calling your dad "Sir", won't it?"

"Yeah, I suppose," Daniel mumbled. He couldn't believe his luck: Rachael wanted to be his friend. Daniel thought secondary school might not be so bad after all.

Answer these questions about the text that you've just read.
Circle the letter of the correct answer.

1. Which word best describes how Daniel feels at the start of the passage?

A Anxious
B Excited
C Unlucky
D Confident
E Angry

/ 1

2. Which of these statements is true?

A There is a beast in the school hall.
B Daniel cannot see the school hall.
C There are no other children in the corridor.
D Daniel wears glasses.
E Daniel's father is in the corridor.

3. Which word best describes what Daniel's father looks like?

A Bald
B Tall
C Thin
D Short
E Broad

4. Daniel tells Rachael that his name is Dennis at first. Why do you think he does this?

A She approached him from behind so he was surprised.
B He doesn't want to be Rachael's friend.
C His middle name is Dennis.
D He was nervous because she was so pretty.
E He did not like being called Daniel.

5. How does Daniel think the other pupils will treat him?

A They will be kind and friendly.
B They will be nervous but welcoming.
C They will be unkind and unfriendly.
D They will be strange and mumbling.
E They won't know what to say to him.

6. How do you think Rachael's brother Tom knows what the headmaster is like?

A Tom is a friend of Daniel's.
B He has heard what the headmaster is like.
C He already goes to the school.
D The headmaster likes him.
E The headmaster knows Tom's parents.

7. How do you think Daniel feels at the end of the passage?

A Miserable
B Uncomfortable
C Lonely
D Shocked
E Relieved

8. Which of the following facts is given in the passage?

A Rachael's surname
B Daniel's age
C Daniel's surname
D The name of Daniel's new form tutor
E What Daniel's uniform looks like

/ 7

Carry on to the next question → →

Answer these questions about the way words and phrases are used in the passage.

9. Which of these words is closest in meaning to "address" (line 5)?

A Direction
B Place
C Speech
D Warning
E Location

10. Which of these words is closest in meaning to "severe" (line 6)?

A Unreasonable
B Dangerous
C Miserable
D Thin
E Strict

11. Which of these is closest in meaning to "simultaneously" (line 9)?

A One after the other
B In an effective way
C In a busy way
D By sharing the tasks
E At the same time

12. "The corridor was like the throat of a terrifying beast" (lines 2-3).
This is an example of:

A a simile.
B a metaphor.
C alliteration.
D an exclamation.
E a pun.

13. "Don't you know your own name?" (line 14).
This is an example of:

A onomatopoeia.
B personification.
C a rhetorical question.
D a proverb.
E a cliché.

14. Rachael says "his bark is worse than his bite" (line 16).
What do you think this phrase means?

A The headmaster only punishes those who deserve it.
B The headmaster has a bad temper.
C The headmaster never punishes anyone.
D The headmaster is not as scary as he seems.
E The headmaster barks when he's angry.

/ 6

Read this poem carefully and answer the questions that follow.

Adapted from 'The Brook'

By thirty hills I hurry down,
Or slip between the ridges,
By twenty thorpes*, a little town,
And half a hundred bridges.

5 Till last by Philip's farm I flow
To join the brimming river,
For men may come and men may go,
But I go on for ever.

I chatter over stony ways,
10 In little sharps and trebles,
I bubble into eddying bays,
I babble on the pebbles.

I chatter, chatter as I flow
To join the brimming river,
15 For men may come and men may go,
But I go on for ever.

I steal by lawns and grassy plots,
I slide by hazel covers;
I move the sweet forget-me-nots
20 That grow for happy lovers.

I slip, I slide, I gloom, I glance,
Among my skimming swallows;
I make the netted sunbeam dance
Against my sandy shallows.

25 And out again I curve and flow
To join the brimming river,
For men may come and men may go,
But I go on for ever.

by Alfred, Lord Tennyson

*thorpes — *small villages*

Answer these questions about the text that you've just read.
Circle the letter of the correct answer.

15. How many bridges does the brook flow under?

A One hundred
B One hundred and fifty
C Twenty
D Fifty
E Thirty

16. What are we told about the brook in verse 2?

A It flows over stones.
B It does not pass any buildings.
C It flows into a different river.
D It dries up.
E Men like to sit and watch it flow by.

/ 2

Carry on to the next question → →

17. Which of the following statements is false?

    A There are fish in the brook.
    B The brook twists and turns.
    C The brook passes by gardens.
    D The brook passes by villages.
    E The brook passes by a farm.

18. What sort of land does the brook flow over in verse 3?

    A It is steep and hilly.
    B It is marshy and boggy.
    C It is soft and sandy.
    D It is thick with mud.
    E It is covered in stones.

19. What sort of river does the brook flow into?

    A A shallow river with a sandy bed.
    B A river that is almost overflowing.
    C A wide and deep river.
    D A long and winding river.
    E A fast-flowing river.

20. What kind of weather is mentioned in the poem?

    A Raindrops
    B Clouds
    C Hail stones
    D Sunbeams
    E Gusts of wind

21. What does the brook sound like in verse 4?

    A People talking
    B Birds singing
    C People laughing
    D Men walking
    E People shouting

22. "For men may come and men may go,
    But I go on for ever" (lines 7-8).
    What do these lines mean?

    A Lots of men cross the bridges over the brook.
    B There is a lot of activity around the brook.
    C The brook passes by lots of men because it is so long.
    D The brook will always be there, no matter what happens to the people.
    E There will always be men living near the brook.

/ 6

Answer these questions about the way words and phrases are used in the passage.

23. What does the word "skimming" (line 22) mean?

A To glide across a surface
B To dive into
C To dip into
D To sit near
E To sing sweetly

24. Which of these is closest in meaning to the word "babble" (line 12)?

A Wash over
B Jump and leap
C Grind and scrape
D Drip slowly
E Make noise continuously

25. What are "plots" (line 17)?

A Vegetable patches
B Formal gardens
C River banks
D Pieces of land
E Gentle slopes

26. What type of word is "hurry" (line 1)?

A Adjective
B Proper noun
C Adverb
D Verb
E Common noun

27. "I chatter, chatter as I flow" (line 13).
What is this phrase an example of?

A Personification
B A simile
C A metaphor
D Alliteration
E A rhyme

28. In the line "Till last by Philip's farm I flow" (line 5),
which word is a pronoun?

A Till
B by
C Philip's
D farm
E I

/ 6

Carry on to the next question →→

In this passage, there are some spelling mistakes. Circle the letter which matches the part of the sentence with the mistake. If there's no mistake, circle N.

29. I wish to complane about a journey that I made yesterday on one of your trains. It was a most

A B C D N

30. unpleasant experience from begining to end. The train was delayed by two hours with no

A B C D N

31. explanation, and I had to stand and wait on a freezing platform. When the train finally

A B C D N

32. made an appearence, it was so busy that I could not find a seat, even though I had booked

A B C D N

33. one in advance. Once I managed to squeeze myself threw to the buffet car, the only choice

A B C D N

34. for lunch was a stale ham and cheese sandwich. I look forward to recieving your response.

A B C D N

/ 6

In this passage, there are some punctuation mistakes. Circle the letter which matches the part of the sentence with the mistake. If there's no mistake, circle N.

35. Most species of Frog live on land but usually lay their eggs in water. These eggs are

A B C D N

36. called 'frogspawn' and resemble clear ball's of jelly with a black dot at the centre. This dot

A B C D N

37. quickly begins to grow a head and tail. Next, it hatches from the egg as a tadpole. As the

A B C D N

38. tadpole develops into a frog, several changes occur the gills become covered with skin; the

A B C D N

39. back and front legs begin to grow: and the eyes become more pronounced. Eventually the

A B C D N

40. tadpoles tail disappears and it looks like a small adult frog. It can then climb out of the water.

A B C D N

/ 6

Choose the right word or phrase to complete this passage.
Circle the letter which matches the correct word.

41. The toy shop was dark **accept** (A) **except** (B) **expect** (C) **apart** (D) **not** (E) for the flickering lights of the

42. electronic toys. Alex and Sandra crept **into** (A) **by** (B) **under** (C) **off** (D) **out** (E) from their hiding place

43. **inside** (A) **between** (B) **among** (C) **behind** (D) **on** (E) a giant stuffed panda. A few moments earlier,

44. **they'd** (A) **it** (B) **they're** (C) **they've** (D) **they'll** (E) watched Mrs Dooley, the owner of the shop, close the

45. front door and turn her key in the lock. Then they **will** (A) **would** (B) **had** (C) **have** (D) **were** (E) listened

46. intently as the sound of her footsteps had **became** (A) **become** (B) **been** (C) **begun** (D) **be** (E) fainter

47. until all was silent. They **could** (A) **can't** (B) **couldn't** (C) **cannot** (D) **can** (E) quite believe they

48. **we're** (A) **was** (B) **were** (C) **where** (D) **will** (E) alone in Dooley's Emporium, the best toy shop in town. The

49. friends looked at each other, **their** (A) **there** (B) **they're** (C) **those** (D) **whose** (E) eyes wide with amazement

50. and disbelief. They didn't know **those** (A) **witch** (B) **that** (C) **whose** (D) **which** (E) toys to play with first.

/10

Total / 50

End of Test

Assessment Test 2

Allow 50 minutes to do this test and work as quickly and as carefully as you can.

You can print **multiple-choice answer sheets** for these questions from our website — go to cgpbooks.co.uk/11plus/answer-sheets or scan the QR code on the right. If you'd prefer to answer the questions on the page, just follow the instructions in the question.

Read this passage carefully and answer the questions that follow.

Tombs of the Ancient Kings

Over four and a half thousand years ago, ancient Egyptians began building pyramids. The pharaohs intended the pyramids to be impressive monuments: eternal resting places to safeguard their souls. Wealthy Egyptians would fill their tombs with the things they would need in the afterlife, but they believed that before their souls were granted eternal life, their actions on Earth were judged rigorously.
5 This judgement happened in the underworld, where the deceased person's heart was weighed against the feather of the goddess Ma'at. If the heart was heavier than the feather, it was deemed unworthy and the person could not enter the afterlife.

Djoser's Step Pyramid was one of the first of these tombs. It is known as a step pyramid because it was built as a series of six successively smaller squares on top of one another. The burial chamber
10 is hidden underground and sealed with a stone weighing 3.5 tonnes, but this did not deter the grave robbers. When the tomb was excavated, almost nothing was left inside.

Perhaps the most famous tomb is the Great Pyramid of Giza, the largest of three pyramids built on the banks of the Nile. By the time it was built, the Egyptians had abandoned the crude stepped design and were building increasingly larger and more imposing structures.

15 The Great Pyramid at Giza took over twenty years to complete and is 146 metres high. It was the tallest building in the world for over 3,800 years and is the only one of the Seven Wonders of the Ancient World that is still standing.

Answer these questions about the text that you've just read.
Circle the letter of the correct answer.

1. Why did the pharaohs build the pyramids?

   A To hide their belongings from grave robbers.
   B To keep their souls safe after they died.
   C So they would become a Wonder of the Ancient World.
   D As great palaces to live in.
   E To show how powerful Egypt was.

2. According to the passage, which statement about Djoser's Step Pyramid is true?

   A It took over twenty years to complete.
   B It was built by foreign slaves.
   C It is an early example of a pyramid.
   D It was the tallest building in the world at the time.
   E The burial chamber is in the top of the pyramid.

/ 2

3. Why do you think there was nothing left inside the burial chamber when Djoser's Step Pyramid was excavated?

   A The Egyptians were not good at preserving bodies.
   B Djoser was not buried with many valuables.
   C The tomb was raided and the valuables were stolen.
   D Everything had crumbled to dust.
   E The burial chamber was hidden underground.

4. According to the passage, where were the pyramids of Giza built?

   A In the middle of the desert
   B On the coast
   C In the city
   D Close to the river
   E Underground

5. According to the passage, which of these statements about the Great Pyramid is false?

   A It is 146 metres high.
   B It is the last remaining Wonder of the Ancient World.
   C It is the largest of the three pyramids built on the banks of the Nile.
   D It is famous.
   E It is 3,800 years old.

6. According to the passage, why did the Ancient Egyptians fill their tombs with objects?

   A As an offering to the gods.
   B To protect their riches from grave robbers.
   C So their riches could be weighed against a feather.
   D So they were prepared for life after death.
   E So that the gods thought they were wealthy and important.

7. According to the passage, what did the Ancient Egyptians believe?

   A If they built pyramids, the gods would be impressed.
   B Sinners were not allowed to enter the afterlife.
   C Pyramids protected the bodies of the dead from the underworld.
   D They would be able to become gods themselves.
   E The taller the pyramid, the closer the deceased was to the gods.

8. In which paragraph(s) in this passage can you find information about why the pyramids were built?

   A Paragraphs 2 and 3
   B Paragraph 1 only
   C Paragraph 4 only
   D Paragraphs 1 and 4
   E Paragraph 2 only

/ 6

Carry on to the next question →→

Answer these questions about the way words and phrases are used in the passage.

9. Which of these words is closest in meaning to "rigorously" (line 4)?

A Quickly
B Instantly
C Thoroughly
D Partially
E Harshly

10. Which of these words is closest in meaning to "crude" (line 13)?

A Impressive
B Rough
C Cruel
D Ancient
E Complicated

11. Which of these words is closest in meaning to "imposing" (line 14)?

A Holy
B Honorary
C Long-lasting
D Impressive
E Decorative

12. What type of word is "Nile" (line 13)?

A Common noun
B Plural
C Pronoun
D Proper noun
E Collective noun

13. In the line, "If the heart was heavier than the feather" (line 6), which word is a verb?

A If
B heart
C was
D heavier
E than

14. What type of words are these?

rigorously successively increasingly

A Adjectives
B Verbs
C Prepositions
D Nouns
E Adverbs

/ 6

Read this passage carefully and answer the questions that follow.

A Brave Step Forward

It was September, 1921. Eighteen-year-old Antonio and his friend Manolo were very excited; several weeks ago they had left their families on the island of Trinidad and had crossed the Atlantic Ocean in a small cargo ship carrying spices. The journey had been very arduous and he would be glad to reach dry land; he had suffered from sea-sickness on the stormier days of the journey.

5 Now that they had nearly reached Plymouth, Antonio's thoughts turned to his departure from Trinidad all those weeks ago. His mother had hugged him goodbye at the port, and had whispered in his ear that she had promised herself she wouldn't cry because she aspired to be as strong and courageous as he was. But as he stood on the deck of the ship waving farewell to his family, he tasted salty tears in his mouth and he felt an ache in his chest.

10 Although leaving his family had been very difficult, Antonio thought that he had made the right decision. After several years of taking intensive examinations at school, they had been told that they were ready to train as doctors. Antonio's father, who was a doctor himself and had always hoped that at least one of his two children would follow in his footsteps, had advised them that the best place to undertake medical training was London, in one of the big teaching hospitals.

15 As the boat neared the dock, Antonio began to feel slightly apprehensive. He had never left Trinidad before and he had not been away from his parents for any substantial length of time. He thought of his mother and his younger sister, Rosa; they seemed a long way away. He knew he was arriving in Plymouth but he did not have an inkling of how to reach London from there, or where they would spend the night when they arrived there. The closer they came to the dock, the more he felt **20** the knots in his stomach tighten. He had taken a huge step, but was it the right one?

Answer these questions about the text that you've just read.
Circle the letter of the correct answer.

15. Why didn't Antonio's mother cry when he left?

A She was pleased that her son was leaving.
B She didn't want Antonio to think she was weak.
C She wanted to be as brave as Antonio.
D She was proud that he was ambitious.
E She was happy that he would be a doctor.

16. Why was Antonio glad that his journey was nearly over?

A He was looking forward to seeing England.
B He had found the journey long and he had been ill.
C He wanted to visit London.
D He was starting to miss his family.
E He wanted to start his medical training.

/ 2

Carry on to the next question → →

17. Which of the following is not mentioned in the text?

A Where the boys had come from.
B Which ocean they had sailed across.
C How old Manolo is.
D The boys' final destination.
E How Antonio feels about reaching England.

18. Where was Antonio's final destination?

A A hospital in London
B Plymouth
C Trinidad
D A hotel in London
E School

19. How do you think Antonio's father felt about Antonio leaving home?

A Despondent
B Conceited
C Proud
D Annoyed
E Jealous

20. Which of the following statements about the boys' journey is not true?

A The journey was stormy.
B The journey was long.
C The boys travelled on a large ship.
D The first stop on the journey was Plymouth.
E The ship carried passengers and cargo.

21. Which of the following statements is true?

A Antonio was the oldest child in his family.
B Antonio had a brother.
C Antonio's mother was a doctor.
D Antonio's mother was called Rosa.
E Antonio was an only child.

22. Why do you think Antonio felt "an ache in his chest" (line 9)?

A His parents had sacrificed a lot so that he could go to England.
B He hadn't said goodbye to his father.
C He was excited about going to England.
D He had lied to his mother about where he was going.
E Because he wasn't as brave as his mother thought he was.

/ 6

Answer these questions about the way words and phrases are used in the passage.

23. The students took "intensive examinations" (line 11). This means that the examinations were:

A important.
B final.
C detailed.
D expensive.
E demanding.

24. Which of these words is closest in meaning to "apprehensive" (line 15)?

A Frightened
B Nervous
C Excited
D Upset
E Weary

25. Which of these words is closest in meaning to the word "inkling" (line 18)?

A Hope
B Direction
C Idea
D Chance
E Opportunity

26. What type of word is "arduous" (line 3)?

A Verb
B Adjective
C Noun
D Adverb
E Pronoun

27. "As the boat neared the dock" (line 15).
Which word in this sentence is a verb?

A As
B the
C boat
D neared
E dock

28. Antonio "felt the knots in his stomach tighten" (lines 19-20).
What is this phrase an example of?

A A metaphor
B A simile
C A proverb
D A synonym
E An adjective

/ 6

Carry on to the next question →→

Choose the right word or phrase to complete this passage.
Circle the letter which matches the correct word.

29. There are many ways that you can care for **ours** (A) **your** (B) **hour** (C) **are** (D) **you're** (E) environment. Reduce

30. your waste by using a flask in your lunch box **in case** (A) **and** (B) **in spite of** (C) **instead of** (D) **as much as** (E)

31. juice cartons. Reuse materials **whoever** (A) **wherever** (B) **whatever** (C) **whatsoever** (D) **whether** (E) you

32. can, by using old carrier bags for your shopping, for example. **Finally** (A) **But** (B) **However** (C) **So** (D) **Yet** (E) ,

33. recycle paper, glass, cans and any **one** (A) **extra** (B) **another** (C) **less** (D) **other** (E) objects with the recyclable

34. symbol, so that new items **could** (A) **can** (B) **would** (C) **cannot** (D) **won't** (E) be made from used materials.

/ 6

In this passage, there are some punctuation mistakes. Circle the letter which matches the part of the sentence with the mistake. If there's no mistake, circle N.

35. To make these cakes you will need four things: eggs sugar, self-raising flour and butter.
A B C D N

36. Ask an adult to preheat the oven while you line a tray with paper cases! In a bowl, mix
A B C D N

37. together the butter and sugar until light and fluffy. Next, add the egg's, stirring continuously,
A B C D N

38. and then gradually sift in the flour. Once the mixtures smooth, divide it equally between
A B C D N

39. the paper cases. Cook for fifteen to twenty minutes or until golden brown. Once these are
A B C D N

40. cool ice your cakes and decorate with lots of chocolate buttons, sprinkles or jellybeans.
A B C D N

/ 6

In this passage, there are some spelling mistakes. Circle the letter which matches the part of the sentence with the mistake. If there's no mistake, circle N.

41. Please help me to find my ginger tabby cat, Lady Marmalade. She is eigth years old and has
A **B** **C** **D** **N**

42. been missing for a hole week, so I am becoming slightly anxious. I last saw her chasing a
A **B** **C** **D** **N**

43. frightened-looking pigeon accross our lawn; as the bird flew away, Lady M (her nickname)
A **B** **C** **D** **N**

44. jumped straight over the garden fence and dissapeared. If you find her, there are several
A **B** **C** **D** **N**

45. things you need to know. She will only eat homemade meals, so do not feed her disgusting
A **B** **C** **D** **N**

46. tinned food. Her favarite activity is exploring the garden, searching for small frogs and mice,
A **B** **C** **D** **N**

47. so please ensure she has plenty of opportunitys to play outside. Finally, she will definitely
A **B** **C** **D** **N**

48. not sleep in a cat basket because she spends every night on a special cushion on my
A **B** **C** **D** **N**

49. bed and she will become extremeley cross if you attempt to ignore her. Please contact me
A **B** **C** **D** **N**

50. at the enclosed address if you happen to spot her. I will collect her from you imediately.
A **B** **C** **D** **N**

/10

Total / 50

End of Test

Assessment Test 3

Allow 50 minutes to do this test and work as quickly and as carefully as you can.

You can print **multiple-choice answer sheets** for these questions from our website — go to cgpbooks.co.uk/11plus/answer-sheets or scan the QR code on the right. If you'd prefer to answer the questions on the page, just follow the instructions in the question.

Read this passage carefully and answer the questions that follow.

An extract from 'Jane Eyre'

Five o'clock had hardly struck on the morning of the 19th of January, when Bessie brought a candle into my closet and found me already up and nearly dressed. I had risen half-an-hour before her entrance, and had washed my face, and put on my clothes by the light of a half-moon just setting, whose rays streamed through the narrow window near my crib.

5 I was to leave Gateshead that day by a coach which passed the lodge gates at six a.m. Bessie was the only person yet risen; she had lit a fire in the nursery, where she now proceeded to make my breakfast. Few children can eat when excited with the thoughts of a journey; nor could I. Bessie, having pressed me in vain to take a few spoonfuls of the boiled milk and bread she had prepared for me, wrapped some biscuits in a paper and put them into my bag; then she helped me on with my

10 pelisse* and bonnet, and wrapping herself in a shawl, she and I left the nursery.

As we passed Mrs. Reed's bedroom she said, "Will you go in and bid Missis good-bye?"

"No, Bessie: she came to my crib last night when you were gone down to supper, and said I need not disturb her in the morning, or my cousins either; and she told me to remember that she had always been my best friend, and to speak of her and be grateful to her accordingly."

15 "What did you say, Miss?"

"Nothing. I covered my face with the bedclothes, and turned from her to the wall."

"That was wrong, Miss Jane."

"It was quite right, Bessie. Your Missis has not been my friend; she has been my foe."

*pelisse — *winter coat*

by Charlotte Brontë

Answer these questions about the text that you've just read.
Circle the letter that matches the correct answer.

1. At what time did Jane get up?

A Five o'clock
B Half-past four
C Half-past five
D Six o'clock
E Four o'clock

2. According to the passage, what did Jane eat for breakfast?

A Nothing
B Biscuits
C Boiled milk and bread
D Boiled milk
E Bread and butter

/ 2

3. According to the passage, how did Jane dress herself?

A In complete darkness
B By candlelight
C By the light of the moon
D By firelight
E In rays of sunshine

4. Why did Jane not go into Mrs Reed's room to say goodbye?

A Mrs Reed had told her not to.
B Jane had been unhappy at Gateshead.
C Jane was in a hurry to leave.
D It was too early in the morning.
E Jane was too excited.

5. Jane said that she had been right to turn her face to the wall when Mrs Reed spoke to her because:

A she was too angry to talk to her.
B she did not like Mrs Reed.
C she was tired and had to wake up early.
D she didn't want to say something she might regret.
E Mrs Reed had treated Bessie badly.

6. Which word best describes Bessie?

A Bitter
B Helpful
C Excitable
D Sympathetic
E Cheerful

7. Which word best describes how Jane feels about her journey?

A Anxious
B Eager
C Agitated
D Unenthusiastic
E Unhappy

8. Which of the following details is not mentioned in the story?

A Bessie assists Jane with her preparations.
B Jane finds it hard to eat when she's about to travel.
C Jane and Bessie were the only people awake at five o'clock.
D Mrs Reed is Jane's aunt.
E Jane was going to leave at six o'clock.

/ 6

Carry on to the next question → →

Answer these questions about the way words and phrases are used in the passage.

9. Which of these words is closest in meaning to "pressed" (line 8)?

A Suggested
B Encouraged
C Demanded
D Comforted
E Requested

10. What does the word "hardly" mean (line 1)?

A Only just
B Faintly
C Suddenly
D Gradually
E Clearly

11. What is another word for "foe" (line 18)?

A Superior
B Enemy
C Captor
D Rival
E Guardian

12. The moon's rays "streamed through the narrow window near my crib" (line 4).
What is the adjective in this sentence?

A streamed
B through
C narrow
D window
E near

13. What type of word is "children" (line 7)?

A Proper noun
B Collective noun
C Common noun
D Abstract noun
E Pronoun

14. "I covered my face with the bedclothes, and turned from her to the wall" (line 16).
Which are the three prepositions in this sentence?

A "face", "bedclothes" and "wall"
B "I", "face" and "the"
C "I", "my" and "her"
D "covered", "turned" and "to"
E "with", "from" and "to"

/ 6

Read this passage carefully and answer the questions that follow.

Cornwall

Cornwall is a county of dramatic yet contrasting coastlines that can be best explored by walking Britain's longest marked footpath, the South West Coast Path. From here you can experience the breathtaking bays and gently-sloping beaches of the south, as well as the steep cliffs and sea-lashed rocks of the rugged north coast. The northern coastline is sprinkled with resort towns and fishing villages
5 famous for their cobbled streets and pastel-hued harbours, which dot the landscape like jewels.

Inland Cornwall also offers plenty for visitors to experience. Follow the steep lanes that lead to remote villages where you can enjoy a hearty pub lunch. Look for wildlife while dipping your feet into the rivers that meander through cool, wooded valleys. Explore the brooding granite heights of Bodmin Moor and bask in the mild climate that allows rare flora and fauna, including the vibrant
10 Cornish heath, to flourish.

Awash with Celtic heritage, Cornwall's landscape contains many signs of its interesting past. Discover mysterious Bronze Age stone circles and be enchanted by Cornwall's rich folklore — if you're lucky, you might catch a glimpse of a pixie! Feel King Arthur's England come to life by taking a trip to his legendary birthplace at Tintagel. Perched atop wave-battered cliffs, the ruins of Tintagel Castle have
15 fascinated historians, artists and visitors for centuries. Intrepid adventurers can also explore nearby Merlin's Cave, nestled in the cliff-face, where it is said that the wizard Merlin carried a young King Arthur to safety. Cornwall is truly a treasure trove of history and spectacular scenery.

Answer these questions about the text that you've just read.
Circle the letter of the correct answer.

15. According to the passage, which statement about Cornwall is false?

A The roads are flat.
B It is an area of natural beauty.
C Rivers run through forested areas.
D There are villages on the coast and inland.
E It has colourful harbours.

16. The "brooding granite heights of Bodmin Moor" (lines 8-9).
How does this description present the moor?

A Lush and wooded
B Dark and rocky
C Perilous and exposed
D Hilly and cold
E Boggy and muddy

/ 2

Carry on to the next question → →

17. Which of these is not given as a reason to visit Cornwall?

A The chance to see flowers that you can't see elsewhere
B Historical sites
C Pleasant weather
D Scenic walks
E Delicious seafood

18. According to the passage, where was King Arthur born?

A Near the sea
B On the moors
C In a cave
D Near a stone circle
E Close to a harbour

19. "Cornwall is truly a treasure trove of history" (line 17).
What does this phrase mean?

A You can find ancient buried treasure there.
B It used to be an interesting place.
C There is lots of evidence of Cornwall's past.
D There are lots of castles in Cornwall.
E Cornwall is an old county.

20. Which of the following phrases is closest in meaning to "Awash with Celtic heritage" (line 11)?

A A lot of the county's past has been washed away.
B The people of Cornwall are proud of their Celtic heritage.
C There are only a few remaining Celtic heritage sites.
D A lot of Celts live in Cornwall.
E There are lots of reminders of Cornwall's Celtic past.

21. Why do you think Cornwall is described as having "contrasting coastlines" (line 1)?

A The natural beauty of the coast contrasts with Cornwall's historical sites.
B The northern coast is very traditional, but the southern coast is very modern.
C Cornwall's coastline stretches along both the north and south of the county.
D The weather of the northern coastline contrasts with that of the southern coastline.
E The dramatic landscape of the northern coastline contrasts with the coastline in the south.

22. Where would you be most likely to find this text?

A An atlas
B A biography
C An encyclopedia
D A travel brochure
E A book of myths and legends

/ 6

Answer these questions about the way words and phrases are used in the passage.

23. Which of these words is closest in meaning to "remote" (line 7)?

A Isolated
B Beautiful
C Tiny
D Friendly
E Uninhabited

24. The word "meander" (line 8) could most accurately be replaced by:

A gush and tumble.
B flow steadily.
C twist and turn.
D rush quickly.
E trickle slowly.

25. Which of these words is closest in meaning to "Intrepid" (line 15)?

A Reckless
B Courageous
C Resourceful
D Nimble
E Prepared

26. "breathtaking bays and gently-sloping beaches" (line 3).
Which technique is used here?

A Alliteration
B Onomatopoeia
C Personification
D Metaphor
E Simile

27. "Cornwall is truly a treasure trove of history" (line 17).
Which technique is used here?

A Metaphor
B Onomatopoeia
C Irony
D Personification
E Simile

28. What type of words are "steep" (line 6) and "rugged" (line 4)?

A Prepositions
B Adverbs
C Adjectives
D Pronouns
E Conjunctions

/ 6

Carry on to the next question → →

In this passage, there are some spelling mistakes. Circle the letter which matches the part of the sentence with the mistake. If there's no mistake, circle N.

29. Earth is the third planet from the Sun, beyond Mercury and Venus, and the fifth largest planet

A B C D N

30. in the Solar System. It is unique because it is the only planet currently known to sustane life.

A B C D N

31. Conditions on Earth are ideal to support humans, animals and plants. Water, necessery for

A B C D N

32. life, covers approximatley 70% of the Earth's surface. Earth's air is made up of many

A B C D N

33. different gases, including oxygen for us to breath. Also, the distance from the Earth to the

A B C D N

34. Sun means the temprature is neither too hot nor too cold, making it a perfect planet for life.

A B C D N

/ 6

Choose the right word or phrase to complete the passage. Circle the letter which matches the correct word.

35. Oakhill's village fair will take place **today** (A) **yesterday** (B) **tomorrow** (C) **next** (D) **last** (E) afternoon,

36. from 1pm until 3pm, **where** (A) **over** (B) **in** (C) **nearby** (D) **under** (E) the main field at Appleford Farm.

37. As always, there **have** (A) **would** (B) **won't** (C) **will** (D) **is** (E) be an array of items to buy, like Mr May's

38. superb soup made entirely **off** (A) **from** (B) **in** (C) **out** (D) **for** (E) vegetables grown in his garden.

39. There will also be competitions for talented animals. Look **at** (A) **in** (B) **up** (C) **out** (D) **on** (E) for

40. Herbie the sheepdog, who **wins** (A) **won** (B) **winned** (C) **winning** (D) **win** (E) first prize last year.

/ 6

In this passage, there are some punctuation mistakes. Circle the letter which matches the part of the sentence with the mistake. If there's no mistake, circle N.

41. Last night, the resident's of Little Hushing were woken once again by strange noises, which
A B C D N

42. seemed to come from the woods. The small village has now had two weeks of sleepless
A B C D N

43. nights due to the howling and yelping of an unknown creature. Mr Price: the village butcher,
A B C D N

44. said this morning, "It sounds rather like a wild cat. However, his neighbour, Mrs Patel,
A B C D N

45. believes that the noise is in fact a bears fearsome growl. Several sightings of the creature
A B C D N

46. have been recorded. Year 5 children on a nature walk reported a long-armed and big-eared
A B C D N

47. animal swinging through the trees. Conversely, a cyclist, Joe Jones described a large hairy
A B C D N

48. figure with enormous feet plodding slowly along the woodland path. A group of tired, and
A B C D N

49. concerned locals are camping out tonight in the hope of locating the source of the noise and
A B C D N

50. solving the mystery. Whatever it is, lets hope that a hush descends on Little Hushing tonight.
A B C D N

/10

Total / 50

End of Test

Assessment Test 4

Allow 50 minutes to do this test and work as quickly and as carefully as you can.

You can print **multiple-choice answer sheets** for these questions from our website — go to cgpbooks.co.uk/11plus/answer-sheets or scan the QR code on the right. If you'd prefer to answer the questions on the page, just follow the instructions in the question.

Read this passage carefully and answer the questions that follow.

The Crystal Heart

Mi Nuong's father was an influential Lord. He ruled all of the lands of the Red River and his palace stood tall and majestic on its broad, sloping banks. Yet, Mi Nuong was forlorn and melancholy. Her father kept her locked away at the top of the palace's tallest tower in order to keep her out of harm's way. Mi Nuong felt trapped; the only company she had was her maid and her daily routine was always
5 the same. Everyday, she would sit by her window embroidering and look out of her window, gazing sorrowfully down at the waters rushing past far below. Often, she dreamed of being carried away in the fast flowing rapids to distant lands.

One morning, Mi Nuong heard music floating through her open window. She hurried over to see where the sound was coming from. There, on the river below, was a little golden fishing boat. Mi
10 Nuong heard the music rise up from the boat, and caught snatches of a song: "My love is like a blossom in the breeze. My love is like a moonbeam on the waves."

The music was captivating, drawing Mi Nuong like a flickering candle flame draws the unwary moth. The voice was clear and sweet and Mi Nuong leaned out as far out as she could to try to catch sight of the singer. As the boat bobbed past, she glimpsed the tiny figure of a man standing on the prow with a
15 net. A sudden glimmer of hope lit up in her heart and she felt as if she was floating on air. Perhaps this man had come to release her from the tower. Perhaps he was a Mandarin's son in disguise; the man she was destined to marry...

Answer these questions about the text that you've just read.
Circle the letter that matches the correct answer.

1. Why was Mi Nuong lonely?

   A The song she heard reminded her of the world outside.
   B She was confined to the tower.
   C She was tired of her daily routine.
   D Her maid wasn't very good company.
   E She wanted to be rescued by her true love.

2. What does Mi Nuong usually do to pass the time in her tower?

   A She sings.
   B She plays cards.
   C She dreams of her true love.
   D She paints.
   E She sews.

/ 2

3. What is Mi Nuong's father like?

   A Cruel
   B Proud
   C Protective
   D Resentful
   E Arrogant

4. Which one of these things isn't mentioned in the story?

   A Water
   B Fire
   C Sunlight
   D Moonlight
   E Gold

5. How does the music make Mi Nuong feel?

   A Forlorn and lonely
   B Enthralled and wishful
   C Powerful and strong
   D Sorrowful and desperate
   E Lovesick and anxious

6. Why was the man on the boat?

   A He hopes to persuade Mi Nuong to marry him.
   B He has come to sing for Mi Nuong's father.
   C He is delivering goods to the palace.
   D He is fishing in the river.
   E He has come to take Mi Nuong to a distant land.

7. Why does Mi Nuong lean as far out of the window as she can?

   A She wants to hear more of the song.
   B She wants the figure on the fishing boat to see her.
   C She wants to see the singer.
   D She is fascinated by the music.
   E She wants the man on the boat to rescue her.

8. Which of these words best describes how Mi Nuong feels at the end of the passage?

   A Optimistic
   B Relieved
   C Infatuated
   D Besotted
   E Emotional

/ 6

Carry on to the next question → →

Answer these questions about the way words and phrases are used in the passage.

9. Which of these words is closest in meaning to the word "forlorn" (line 2)?

A Distracted
B Furious
C Miserable
D Disappointed
E Abandoned

10. What is meant by the phrase "she felt as if she was floating on air" (line 15)?

A She felt light-headed.
B She felt joyful.
C She couldn't believe what was happening.
D She felt carefree.
E She was in love.

11. What is meant by the phrase "the man she was destined to marry" (lines 16-17)?

A She really wants to marry him.
B She is meant to marry him.
C She is planning to marry him.
D Her father intends her to marry him.
E He has come especially to ask her to marry him.

12. "like a flickering candle flame draws the unwary moth" (line 12).
What technique is being used here?

A A proverb
B Personification
C A simile
D An abbreviation
E A metaphor

13. What type of word is "unwary" (line 12)?

A Adjective
B Adverb
C Noun
D Verb
E Pronoun

14. "she glimpsed the tiny figure of a man standing on the prow" (line 14).
Which of these words is a verb?

A she
B glimpsed
C tiny
D figure
E man

/ 6

Read this passage carefully and answer the questions that follow.

An extract from 'The Secret Garden'

At last the horses began to go more slowly, as if they were climbing up-hill, and presently there seemed to be no more hedges and no more trees. She could see nothing, in fact, but a dense darkness on either side. She leaned forward and pressed her face against the window just as the carriage gave a big jolt.

5 "Eh! We're on the moor now sure enough," said Mrs. Medlock.

The carriage lamps shed a yellow light on a rough-looking road which seemed to be cut through bushes and low-growing things which ended in the great expanse of dark apparently spread out before and around them. A wind was rising and making a singular, wild, low, rushing sound.

"It's—it's not the sea, is it?" said Mary, looking round at her companion.

10 "No, not it," answered Mrs. Medlock. "Nor it isn't fields nor mountains, it's just miles and miles and miles of wild land that nothing grows on but heather and gorse and broom, and nothing lives on but wild ponies and sheep."

"I feel as if it might be the sea, if there were water on it," said Mary. "It sounds like the sea just now."

15 "That's the wind blowing through the bushes," Mrs. Medlock said. "It's a wild, dreary enough place to my mind, though there's plenty that likes it—particularly when the heather's in bloom."

On and on they drove through the darkness, and though the rain stopped, the wind rushed by and whistled and made strange sounds. The road went up and down, and several times the carriage passed over a little bridge beneath which water rushed very fast with a great deal of noise. Mary felt
20 as if the drive would never come to an end and that the wide, bleak moor was a wide expanse of black ocean through which she was passing on a strip of dry land.

"I don't like it," she said to herself. "I don't like it," and she pinched her thin lips more tightly together.

by Frances Hodgson Burnett

Answer these questions about the text that you've just read.
Circle the letter that matches the correct answer.

15. What can Mary see when she first looks out of the carriage?

A Hedges and trees
B Darkness
C The road
D The sea
E The moor

16. Which of these things is not mentioned by Mrs Medlock?

A Moor
B Gorse
C Wind
D Water
E Sheep

/ 2

Carry on to the next question → →

17. How do you think Mary feels as they travel?

A Excited
B Anxious
C Tired
D Sick
E Enthusiastic

18. How is the moor described in the passage?

A Treacherous and boggy
B Full of wildlife
C Untamed and desolate
D Mountainous and bare
E Dry and barren

19. Why does Mary ask "it's not the sea, is it?" (line 9)?

A She can hear seagulls above her.
B She can see nothing but darkness all around.
C She can smell salt in the air.
D She can feel the carriage jolting.
E She can see water out of the window.

20. Which of these best describes the journey?

A Uphill and smooth
B Fast and exciting
C Uncomfortable and lonely
D Strange but interesting
E Long and disorientating

21. What kind of mood does the author create in lines 17-23?

A Unsettling
B Relaxing
C Melancholy
D Terrifying
E Cheerful

22. What kind of text is this?

A Biography
B Travel writing
C A fairy tale
D Fiction
E A diary

/ 6

Answer these questions about the way words and phrases are used in the passage.

23. What is meant by the word "presently" (line 1)?

    A Eventually
    B Later
    C Previously
    D Straight away
    E Before long

24. Which of these words is closest in meaning to the word "expanse" (line 7)?

    A Open
    B View
    C Area
    D Boundary
    E Horizon

25. Which of these words is closest in meaning to "singular" (line 8)?

    A Strange
    B Loud
    C Quiet
    D Lonely
    E Exciting

26. "the carriage passed over a little bridge beneath which water rushed" (lines 18-19).
    Which of the words in this sentence is a preposition?

    A the
    B carriage
    C little
    D beneath
    E rushed

27. "the wide, bleak moor was a wide expanse of black ocean" (lines 20-21).
    What technique is used here?

    A A simile
    B A metaphor
    C An allusion
    D Onomatopoeia
    E A cliché

28. What type of words are these?

    ponies **sheep** **mountains** **bushes**

    A Abstract nouns
    B Proper nouns
    C Common nouns
    D Collective nouns
    E Pronouns

/ 6

Carry on to the next question → →

In this passage, there are some spelling mistakes. Circle the letter which matches the part of the sentence with the mistake. If there's no mistake, circle N.

29. The Adventure Trail at Door Hall has the best mountain biking routes in the region. With tough
A B C D N

30. climbs to the summit through dense forests, followed by exhilarating desents along the
A B C D N

31. River Door, with plentyful rest stops on the way. The trail takes 3 hours, ideal for an active
A B C D N

32. day out. There's a whole range of routes including a begginners' circuit with gentle inclines,
A B C D N

33. and a mini safari around the park boundaries which passes our residant African elephants.
A B C D N

34. Our hire shop stocks bicycles and accessories and there's a restaraunt serving family favourites.
A B C D N

/ 6

In this passage, there are some punctuation mistakes. Circle the letter which matches the part of the sentence with the mistake. If there's no mistake, circle N.

35. "Why is it called 'The Dragons' Chamber'?" Asked Ian, shining his torch around the cave.
A B C D N

36. "Because of the dragons, of course," Jess said scornfully. "There's supposed to have been
A B C D N

37. a whole family which terrorised the valley for years until they died from some weird disease"
A B C D N

38. Peering into the gloom of the cavern, Ian shivered. It was huge the light from his torch
A B C D N

39. barely reached the far walls. Vicious-looking stalactites hung from it's ceiling. As he
A B C D N

40. listened, he thought, he heard, from deep inside the mountain, a faint but distinct rumbling.
A B C D N

/ 6

Choose the right word or phrase to complete the passage.
Circle the letter which matches the correct word.

Dear Diary,

41. Today was my first day at my new school and it **be** (A) **was** (B) **does** (C) **went** (D) **were** (E) awful. First, I

42. missed the bus. It's what we were all worried **we'd done** (A) **I'd do** (B) **we'd do** (C) **we did** (D) **we'll do** (E) ,

43. but I actually did it. Mum **has to** (A) **had to** (B) **did** (C) **have to** (D) **must have** (E) drive me to school in her

pink van with 'Pam's Pampered Pooches' on the side.

44. What's **worse** (A) **more worse** (B) **worser** (C) **worst** (D) **most bad** (E) , she kissed me goodbye in front of

45. all the Year 7s who **were** (A) **was** (B) **are** (C) **is** (D) **be** (E) waiting to be shown their form rooms. I wasn't

46. shown mine as I had to take a detour in order **too** (A) **that** (B) **so** (C) **to** (D) **for** (E) wash the lipstick mark

47. **off** (A) **of** (B) **onto** (C) **in** (D) **into** (E) my face, so I got lost. My nice form teacher told everyone off for laughing

48. at me when I fell over a chair. **By** (A) **In** (B) **Despite** (C) **To** (D) **When** (E) lunch, everyone seemed to

49. **had forgot** (A) **have forgotten** (B) **had forgotten** (C) **have forgot** (D) **has forgotten** (E) my disastrous

start, until I opened my lunch box to find 6 biscuits.

50. On each **was wrote** (A) **wrote** (B) **write** (C) **was written** (D) **was writ** (E) a word in bright pink icing.

Together they said, 'Good - Luck - On - Your - First - Day'.

/10

Total / 50

End of Test

Assessment Test 5

Allow 50 minutes to do this test and work as quickly and as carefully as you can.

You can print **multiple-choice answer sheets** for these questions from our website — go to cgpbooks.co.uk/11plus/answer-sheets or scan the QR code on the right. If you'd prefer to answer the questions on the page, just follow the instructions in the question.

Read this poem carefully and answer the questions that follow.

The Way Through the Woods

They shut the road through the woods
Seventy years ago.
Weather and rain have undone it again,
And now you would never know
5 There was once a road through the woods
Before they planted the trees.
It is underneath the coppice and heath,
And the thin anemones.
Only the keeper sees
10 That, where the ring-dove broods,
And the badgers roll at ease,
There was once a road through the woods.

Yet, if you enter the woods
Of a summer evening late,
15 When the night-air cools on the trout-ringed pools
Where the otter whistles his mate.
(They fear not men in the woods
Because they see so few),
You will hear the beat of a horse's feet
20 And the swish of a skirt in the dew,
Steadily cantering through
The misty solitudes,
As though they perfectly knew
The old lost road through the woods...
25 But there is no road through the woods.

by Rudyard Kipling

Answer these questions about the text that you've just read.
Circle the letter that matches the correct answer.

1. Which of the following statements about the road is false?
   There is no road through the woods because:
   A it was closed.
   B the rain has eroded it.
   C trees have been planted over it.
   D horses have worn it away.
   E it has become overgrown.

2. Which of these is not mentioned in the poem?
   A When they shut the road.
   B What the woods are like.
   C The sounds in the wood.
   D Which animals are in the wood.
   E What the road was like.

/ 2

3. What do lines 7-12 focus on?

   A Who shut the road.
   B Why the road was closed.
   C How the poet feels about the woods.
   D What the woods used to be like.
   E What the woods are like now.

4. Which word best describes what the animals in the woods are like?

   A Afraid
   B Endangered
   C Aggressive
   D Solitary
   E Carefree

5. Which adjective best describes the poet's tone in lines 1-2?

   A Pleased
   B Matter-of-fact
   C Cautious
   D Confused
   E Frustrated

6. The poet describes "trout-ringed pools" (line 15). What do you think they are?

   A Pools of water where the otters drink
   B Pools of water surrounded by trees
   C Perfectly round pools of water
   D Pools where fish are rippling the water's surface
   E Muddy puddles of water

7. How do the otters feel about men?

   A Intimidated
   B Indifferent
   C Fearful
   D Positive
   E Angry

8. What is happening in lines 19-24?

   A The poet is lost in the woods.
   B The poet is hunting animals in the woods.
   C The poet is imagining that other people are in the woods.
   D The poet is talking to other people in the woods.
   E The poet is dancing on the road.

/ 6

Carry on to the next question → →

Answer these questions about the way words and phrases are used in the passage.

9. What is "the coppice" (line 7)?

A A small house
B An abandoned building
C Small trees and shrubs
D Wild flowers
E A small lake

10. Which of these is closest in meaning to "broods" (line 10)?

A Sleeps
B Builds nests
C Sings
D Cleans itself
E Hatches eggs

11. "When the night-air cools on the trout-ringed pools" (line 15).
Which of these words is a verb?

A When
B night-air
C cools
D on
E pools

12. "It is underneath the coppice and heath" (line 7).
What type of word is "underneath"?

A Adjective
B Conjunction
C Adverb
D Verb
E Preposition

13. "And the swish of a skirt in the dew," (line 20)
What technique is used here?

A A metaphor
B A simile
C Personification
D A homophone
E Onomatopoeia

14. What is meant by the word "solitudes" (line 22)?

A Dark places
B Lonely places
C Beautiful places
D Foggy places
E Wild places

/ 6

Read this passage carefully and answer the questions that follow.

An extract from 'The Rocking Horse Winner'

There were a boy and two little girls. They lived in a pleasant house, with a garden, and they had discreet servants, and felt themselves superior to anyone in the neighbourhood.

Although they lived in style, they felt always an anxiety in the house. There was never enough money. The mother had a small income, and the father had a small income, but not nearly enough for
5 the social position which they had to keep up. The father went into town to some office. But though he had good prospects, these prospects never materialised. There was always the grinding sense of the shortage of money, though the style was always kept up.

At last the mother said: "I will see if I can't make something." But she did not know where to begin. She racked her brains, and tried this thing and the other, but could not find anything successful.

10 The failure made deep lines come into her face. Her children were growing up, they would have to go to school. There must be more money, there must be more money. The father, who was always very handsome and expensive in his tastes, seemed as if he never would be able to do anything worth doing. And the mother, who had a great belief in herself, did not succeed any better, and her tastes were just as expensive.

15 And so the house came to be haunted by the unspoken phrase: There must be more money! There must be more money!

by D. H. Lawrence

Answer these questions about the text that you've just read.
Circle the letter that matches the correct answer.

15. "But though he had good prospects, these prospects never materialised" (lines 5-6).
What is meant by this?

A The father was a vain man.
B The father was not promoted.
C The father was dismissed from his job.
D The father worked long hours.
E The father did not have any ambitions.

16. Which of the following is not given as a reason why the family needed more money?

A The children would have to go to school.
B The father had expensive tastes.
C The mother had expensive tastes.
D They had a social position to keep up.
E They lived in a big house.

/ 2

Carry on to the next question →→

17. Why do you think the author repeats the phrase, "There must be more money" (lines 15-16)?

A Because the father gets a pay rise.
B Because the family are desperate for money.
C Because they had money but spent it all.
D Because they have expensive tastes.
E Because they have large debts.

18. Why did the mother fail to make money?

A She did not have the skills to make anything.
B She did not want to sell what she had made.
C Everything she tried to make was unsuccessful.
D She didn't have any ideas about what to make.
E She did not have enough money for materials.

19. Which detail shows that the mother was troubled by the lack of money?

A Her face was creased.
B She had a small income.
C She was always deep in thought.
D She stopped spending money.
E She could not make anything.

20. Which of these words best describes the father in the passage?

A Unsuccessful
B Thoughtful
C Downtrodden
D Ambitious
E Practical

21. In the extract it says that "the house came to be haunted by the unspoken phrase: 'There must be more money!'" (line 15). What does this mean?

A There were ghosts in the house.
B All the family could talk about was money.
C The servants were gossips.
D The children were not allowed to ask questions.
E Nobody dared mention the lack of money.

22. According to the passage, the family "felt themselves superior" (line 2). What does this phrase tell us about the family?

A They wanted to be famous.
B They were richer than their neighbours.
C They had the largest house in their street.
D They thought they were better than their neighbours.
E They had better servants than their neighbours.

/ 6

Answer these questions about the way words and phrases are used in the passage.

23. Which of these is closest in meaning to "anxiety" (line 3)?

A Fear
B Worry
C Unhappiness
D Desperation
E Misery

24. The word "discreet" (line 2) could most accurately be replaced by:

A tactful.
B hard-working.
C numerous.
D loyal.
E reliable.

25. Which of these words is closest in meaning to "grinding" (line 6)?

A Painful
B Upsetting
C Annoying
D Relentless
E Awful

26. What type of word is "handsome" (line 12)?

A Verb
B Adverb
C Adjective
D Preposition
E Noun

27. "There was always the grinding sense of the shortage of money, though the style was always kept up." (lines 6-7). Which of these words is a conjunction?

A sense
B money
C style
D though
E always

28. "There must be more money" (line 11).
What kind of phrase is this?

A Abbreviation
B Exclamation
C Analogy
D Command
E Statement

/ 6

Carry on to the next question → →

In this passage, there are some spelling mistakes. Circle the letter which matches the part of the sentence with the mistake. If there's no mistake, circle N.

29. Mr Sugar's sweet shop was packed. Every shelf was laden with jars of multycoloured bon-bons.
A B C D N

30. Children were gazing at the smooth, golden toffees, wrapped in gold paper, and the exsquisite
A B C D N

31. Swiss truffles in guilded boxes. A barrel of gleaming white mints stood by the door opposite a
A B C D N

32. display of golden, freshly baked gingerbread men. There were crunchy honeycomb peices and
A B C D N

33. gobstoppers like ping-pong balls. Mr Sugar presided over it all in his striped apron, doling out
A B C D N

34. ice creams in every flavour, from butterscotch to cherry cream and mango to rasberry ripple.
A B C D N

/ 6

Choose the right word or phrase to complete the passage. Circle the letter which matches the correct word.

35. Ali watched the twin moons **rose** (A) **rise** (B) **arise** (C) **arose** (D) **risen** (E) over the barren landscape.

36. A huge dust cloud **beginning** (A) **begun** (B) **were beginning** (C) **began** (D) **begins** (E) to form in the distance.

37. The atmosphere was charged **of** (A) **from** (B) **with** (C) **in** (D) **under** (E) static electricity and flashes of white

38. light burst repeatedly, **filling** (A) **fills** (B) **filled** (C) **were filling** (D) **fill** (E) the night sky. However long he

39. stayed, Ali **wouldn't** (A) **will** (B) **would** (C) **won't** (D) **has never** (E) get used to the fierce beauty of this planet.

40. He adjusted his night vision goggles and waited **for** (A) **to be** (B) **at** (C) **since** (D) **in** (E) rescue.

/ 6

In this passage, there are some punctuation mistakes. Circle the letter which matches the part of the sentence with the mistake. If there's no mistake, circle N.

41. Skateboarders old and young staged a protest on Friday against developers plans to close
A B C D N

42. a Local skateboard park. Hundreds of people, some as young as seven, gathered with
A B C D N

43. their skateboards outside the council's offices to deliver a petition to the mayor, whose support
A B C D N

44. for the closure has caused fury amongst locals. "That park's our's. It's the only place we've got
A B C D N

45. to practise." said one young protester, "and we're not allowed in the streets." Surprisingly, a
A B C D N

46. number of elderly, residents were there to support the skateboarders' cause. "These youngsters
A B C D N

47. need somewhere to skate," said Elsie Smith, from Dove Close, next to the park. "It's ridiculous!
A B C D N

48. "They've got nowhere else and it stops them from using the road and knocking people over."
A B C D N

49. The skate park which was given a £5,000 'face lift' last May with money raised by local people,
A B C D N

50. includes half pipes, mini ramps, and flat bars, as well as a snack bar and toilets.
A B C D N

/10

Total / 50

End of Test

Assessment Test 6

Allow 50 minutes to do this test and work as quickly and as carefully as you can.

You can print **multiple-choice answer sheets** for these questions from our website — go to cgpbooks.co.uk/11plus/answer-sheets or scan the QR code on the right. If you'd prefer to answer the questions on the page, just follow the instructions in the question.

Read this passage carefully and answer the questions that follow.

If You Go Down to the Woods Today

Arguments continue to rage as to whether big cats such as panthers, pumas, leopards and lynx are stalking the British countryside. Hundreds, if not thousands, of anxious members of the public have reported sightings of these creatures, and stories of unexplained attacks on livestock continue to appear in local newspapers. Reported sightings come from all over the United Kingdom but some
5 areas produce more reports of mysterious creatures than others, leading to local legends such as Cornwall's famous Beast of Bodmin.

For many, these large felines living in our midst are no more than rural myth and the reports are dismissed as hoaxes, mistakes or fantasies. However, not everybody rejects the idea that these big cats might be living wild in remote parts of our countryside. An increasing number of people believe
10 that there are too many witnesses for the rumours to be unfounded. They also point out that several sightings and reports of attacks on livestock originate from farmers; people who may not know much about big cats but who do know the countryside well.

There are various theories about how these exotic creatures may have come to be resident in our countryside. Some believe that the animals might have escaped from zoos or wildlife parks.
15 Another explanation is that owners abandoned the wild animals when they became too large to handle, or released them when the Dangerous Wild Animals Act was introduced in the 1970s. It's possible that these owners travelled to remote areas of the country where they released animals that they were no longer permitted to keep.

Answer these questions about the text that you've just read.
Circle the letter that matches the correct answer.

1. Which of the following is given as evidence for the existence of big cats in the wild?

   A Local legend
   B Newspaper reports
   C Anxious people
   D Attacks on animals
   E Rumours

2. How do people who have reported sightings feel about the possibility of wild cats living in Britain?

   A Enraged
   B Concerned
   C Confused
   D Sceptical
   E Indecisive

/ 2

3. Which of the following is not given as a possible reason for the reported sightings?

A The sightings are real.
B The sightings are jokes.
C The sightings are dreams.
D The sightings are errors.
E The sightings are lies.

4. What reason is given for the growing number of people who believe the reports?

A The reports have been published in local newspapers, so more people have read them.
B The number of attacks on livestock has increased.
C The existence of the Beast of Bodmin has been proven.
D Several big cats have escaped from zoos, so they must be living in the wild.
E There are many reports, so people think they can't all be false.

5. According to the passage, which of the following statements is true?

A The big cats have attacked members of the public.
B The attacks on livestock made national news.
C No reports have come from Scotland.
D The Beast of Bodmin is a wild cat.
E Many sightings have come from Cornwall.

6. According to the passage, what are the farmers' reports like?

A Trustworthy, because they are familiar with the land.
B Accurate, because they have good eyesight.
C Reliable, because they live in remote places.
D Mistaken, because they spread rumours.
E Unreliable, because they don't know much about big cats.

7. Why might owners have released big cats after the Dangerous Wild Animals Act was introduced?

A Their animals were too dangerous to keep.
B The Act allowed the big cats to live only in remote areas.
C Keeping big cats became illegal.
D They were worried their big cats would attack livestock.
E The animals grew too big to be kept indoors.

8. Why do you think the writer says that "Arguments continue to rage" (line 1)?

A Nobody can agree what kind of animal they have seen.
B There have been many sightings in the past.
C People feel strongly about the issue.
D Farmers are angry about losing livestock.
E Most people argue that wild cats exist.

/ 6

Carry on to the next question → →

Answer these questions about the way words and phrases are used in the passage.

9. Which of these words is closest in meaning to "rural" (line 7)?

A Suburban
B Rustic
C Uncommon
D Ancient
E Wild

10. Which of these words is closest in meaning to "mysterious" (line 5)?

A Concealed
B Reserved
C Impossible
D Inexplicable
E Fabricated

11. Which word could most accurately replace "exotic" (line 13)?

A Dangerous
B Foreign
C Wild
D Native
E Exciting

12. What type of noun is "United Kingdom" (line 4)?

A Proper noun
B Common noun
C Collective noun
D Pronoun
E Abstract noun

13. Which word best describes this type of article?

A Biased
B Factual
C Insulting
D Mythical
E Judgemental

14. What part of speech is "Wild" (line 16)?

A Adverb
B Adjective
C Noun
D Verb
E Pronoun

/ 6

Read this poem carefully and answer the questions that follow.

The Tiger

Tiger, tiger, burning bright
In the forests of the night,
What immortal hand or eye
Could frame thy fearful symmetry?

5 In what distant deeps or skies
Burnt the fire of thine eyes?
On what wings dare he aspire?
What the hand dare seize the fire?

And what shoulder and what art,
10 Could twist the sinews of thy heart?
And, when thy heart began to beat,
What dread hand and what dread feet?

What the hammer? what the chain?
In what furnace was thy brain?
15 What the anvil? what dread grasp
Dare its deadly terrors clasp?

When the stars threw down their spears,
And watered heaven with their tears,
Did He smile His work to see?
20 Did He who made the lamb make thee?

Tiger, tiger, burning bright
In the forests of the night,
What immortal hand or eye
Dare frame thy fearful symmetry?

by William Blake

Answer these questions about the text that you've just read.
Circle the letter that matches the correct answer.

15. Which of these statements best describes how the poet feels about the tiger?

A The poet is disgusted by the tiger.
B The poet is jealous of the tiger.
C The poet loves the tiger.
D The poet hates the tiger.
E The poet is afraid of the tiger.

16. Which of the following does the poet not ask about?

A Who made the tiger
B Where the tiger was made
C How the tiger was made
D When the tiger was made
E What was used to make the tiger

/ 2

Carry on to the next question →→

17. What do lines 23-24 suggest about the tiger's creator?

A He is uncertain about the tiger.
B He is violent towards the tiger.
C He is brave to have made the tiger.
D He is proud of the tiger.
E He regrets creating the tiger.

18. Why are the "hammer", "chain", "furnace" and "anvil" mentioned in verse 4?

A These tools were needed to make the tiger.
B The poet compares making a tiger to the work of a blacksmith.
C They are weapons full of "deadly terrors".
D The poet is comparing the tiger's paws to weapons.
E The creator used to be a blacksmith.

19. "Did He smile His work to see?" (line 19).
This question is asking:

A How the tiger felt after being created.
B How the tiger felt after seeing the stars.
C Whether the stars were happy when the tiger was made.
D How the tiger's creator felt after making the animal.
E Why the tiger's creator is happy.

20. "Did He who made the lamb make thee?" (line 20).
This question is asking:

A If the lamb was made before the tiger.
B If the tiger was made before the lamb.
C If the tiger and the lamb are actually so different.
D If the creator preferred the lamb or the tiger.
E If the same creator made the tiger and the lamb.

21. Who do you think the poet is addressing in the poem?

A The lamb
B The tiger
C The tiger's creator
D The reader
E Himself

22. Why do you think the poem is made up of unanswered questions?

A The tiger's creator refuses to answer the poet.
B The tiger cannot answer the poet.
C The tiger's creator is now in heaven.
D The poet won't wait for the tiger's creator to answer.
E The creation of the tiger is beyond human understanding.

/ 6

Answer these questions about the way words and phrases are used in the passage.

23. Which of these words is closest in meaning to “immortal” (line 3)?

A Enduring
B Transitory
C Powerful
D Temporary
E Evolving

24. Which of these words is closest in meaning to “twist” (line 10)?

A Move
B Wind
C Make
D Reverse
E Unravel

25. Which of these words is closest in meaning to “seize” (line 8)?

A Conquer
B Hold
C Steal
D Grasp
E Touch

26. What part of speech is “began” (line 11)?

A Adverb
B Preposition
C Adjective
D Noun
E Verb

27. What technique is used in the line “frame thy fearful symmetry” (line 4)?

A Metaphor
B Cliché
C Analogy
D Alliteration
E Simile

28. The poet says that “the stars threw down their spears” (line 17).
What technique is this?

A Irony
B Onomatopoeia
C Personification
D Proverb
E Abbreviation

/ 6

Carry on to the next question → →

In this passage, there are some punctuation mistakes. Circle the letter which matches the part of the sentence with the mistake. If there's no mistake, circle N.

29. You're invited to the grand opening of Mr Tate's Magical Emporium tonight at six 'o clock.
A B C D N

30. You'll find a range of fantastical, fabulous and phenomenal tricks: 'Magical Fingers' (to
A B C D N

31. terrify teachers; trick card decks (to confound friends); gruesome gags like thumb tips',
A B C D N

32. eyeballs and fake blood; and a variety of trick soaps in night, black, blood red and sick green.
A B C D N

33. Mr Tate himself will be here to advise. Whether youre a beginner or a master magician, why
A B C D N

34. not visit us at the best magic store in town and conjure up 20% discount with this advert.
A B C D N

/ 6

Choose the right word or phrase to complete the passage. Circle the letter which matches the correct word.

35. There are a few things you will need **during** **after** **when** **before** **while** you can buy a hamster.
A B C D E

36. You **would** **may** **will** **must** **could** have a cage with enough space for them to sleep and play.
A B C D E

37. You'll also need the right food. Hamsters' eating habits **are** **is** **be** **was** **our** simple. They eat
A B C D E

38. dry food made **by** **in** **have** **to** **from** seeds and grains with occasional bits of raw vegetables
A B C D E

39. and fruit as a treat. **Finally** **After** **Before** **Because** **Yet** hamsters need exercise; running
A B C D E

40. around in a ball is ideal, **so** **when** **if** **although** **but** you should consider getting one.
A B C D E

/ 6

In this passage, there are some spelling mistakes. Circle the letter which matches the part of the sentence with the mistake. If there's no mistake, circle N.

41. Cleo had a vivid imagenation so it was no surprise when she announced that she would be late

A B C D N

42. for tea on Friday because she was going on a school trip to a distent galaxy. The trip was free as

A B C D N

43. the alien pupils were providing the spaceship and accomodation. She would require a packed

A B C D N

44. lunch and sevaral changes of clothes as they would be travelling for centuries. Smirking,

A B C D N

45. Mum sugested putting Astronaut Lollipops in her lunch box. Dad joked about weighing down

A B C D N

46. her trainers. Cleo just smiled that secritive smile she reserved for occasions when they clearly

A B C D N

47. didn't believe her. The next week, Mum waited patiently with the other parents. At six o'clock,

A B C D N

48. there was a brief shudder and a gentle whisper of air, then fourty excited children emerged out

A B C D N

49. of nowhere accompanied by an identical number of bright blue aliens with enormous eyes.

A B C D N

50. "Didn't I mention," asked Cleo as Mum's jaw visably dropped, "it's an exchange visit?"

A B C D N

/10

Total / 50

End of Test

Glossary

abbreviation	A shortened version of a word, e.g. "bike" instead of "bicycle".
adjective	A word that describes a noun, e.g. "beautiful morning", "frosty lawn".
adverb	A word that describes a verb or an adjective, e.g. "He ran quickly."
alliteration	The repetition of a sound at the beginning of words within a phrase, e.g. "Lovely Lois likes lipstick."
antonym	A word that has the opposite meaning to another, e.g. "good" and "bad".
comparative	A word that compares one thing with another, e.g. "shorter", "worse".
conjunction	A word that joins two clauses, e.g. "and", "but".
fiction	Text that has been made up by the author, about imaginary people and events.
homographs	Words that are spelt the same, but have different meanings, e.g. row (argue/paddle).
homophones	Words that sound the same, but mean different things, e.g. "hair" and "hare".
idiom	A phrase which doesn't literally mean what it says, e.g. "raining cats and dogs".
imagery	Language that creates a vivid picture in the reader's mind.
irony	When a writer says the opposite of what they mean, or when the opposite happens to what the reader expects.
metaphor	A way of describing something by saying that it is something else, e.g. "John's legs were lead weights."
non-fiction	Text that is about facts and real people and events.
noun	A word that names something, e.g. "Paul", "scissors", "flock", "loyalty".
onomatopoeia	When words sound like the noise they describe, e.g. "pop", "bang", "squelch".
personification	A way of describing something by giving it human feelings and characteristics, e.g. "The cruel wind plucked remorselessly at my threadbare clothes."
prefix	Letters that can be put in front of a word to change its meaning, e.g. "unlock".
preposition	A word that tells you how things are related, e.g. "in", "above", "before", "of".
pronoun	Words that can be used instead of nouns, e.g. "I", "you", "he", "it".
proverb	A short well-known saying that may give advice, e.g. "There's no point crying over spilt milk."
rhetorical question	A question that doesn't need an answer, e.g. "When will they learn?"
simile	A way of describing something by comparing it to something else, e.g. "The stars were like a thousand diamonds, glittering in the sky."
subject	The person or thing doing the action of a verb, e.g. "Jo laughed", "the bird flew".
subordinate clause	A less important bit of the sentence which doesn't make sense on its own.
suffix	Letters that can be put after a word to change its meaning, e.g. "playful" .
superlative	A word that refers to the most or least of a group of things, e.g. "the best team".
synonym	A word with a similar meaning to another word, e.g. "big" and "huge".
verb	An action or being word, e.g. "I run", "he went", "you are".

Answers

Page 2 — Parts of Speech

1) **when he heard the strange whirring noise** — This is the subordinate clause because it doesn't make sense on its own.
2) **after drinking the sickly cough medicine** — This is the subordinate clause because it doesn't make sense on its own.
3) **When the dog had finished gnawing the bone** — This is the subordinate clause because it doesn't make sense on its own.
4) **so that he could reach** — This is the subordinate clause because it doesn't make sense on its own.
5) **After the police had departed** — This is the subordinate clause because it doesn't make sense on its own.
6) **even though it is dangerous** — This is the subordinate clause because it doesn't make sense on its own.
7) **While nobody was looking** — This is the subordinate clause because it doesn't make sense on its own.
8) **As soon as we had pitched the tent** — This is the subordinate clause because it doesn't make sense on its own.
9) **while the neighbours are out** — This is the subordinate clause because it doesn't make sense on its own.
10) **proper noun** — 'Germany' is a proper noun because it is the name of a place.
11) **collective noun** — 'herd' is a collective noun because it is the name for a group of cows.
12) **common noun** — 'house' is a common noun because it is a name for an object.
13) **abstract noun** — 'honesty' is an abstract noun because it is a name for something you can't experience with your five senses.
14) **collective noun** — 'range' is a collective noun because it is the name for a group of mountains.
15) **abstract noun** — 'Hunger' is an abstract noun because it is a name for something you can't experience with your five senses — it only has a capital letter because it is at the start of a sentence.
16) **collective noun** — 'team' is a collective noun because it is a name for a group of people.
17) **common noun** — 'doughnuts' is a common noun because it is a name for an object — it is in the plural form here.
18) **proper noun** — 'Bristol' is a proper noun because it is the name of a place.

Page 3 — Parts of Speech

1) **preposition** — 'around' is a preposition here because it tells you where the committee sat in relation to the table.
2) **adverb** — 'early' is an adverb here because it describes how Pavel arrived.
3) **adjective** — 'concerned' is an adjective here because it describes the noun in the sentence — 'Mary'.
4) **adjective** — 'talented' is an adjective here because it describes the noun in the sentence — 'The octopus'.
5) **preposition** — 'above' is a preposition here because it tells you where the eagle flew in relation to the mountains.
6) **adverb** — 'Frantically' is an adverb here because it describes how the person searched.
7) **adjective** — 'smart' is an adjective here because it describes the pronoun in the sentence — 'he'.
8) **preposition** — 'through' is a preposition here because it tells you where the baby wandered in relation to the door.
9) **adverb** — 'nervously' is an adverb here because it describes how Anjali contemplated.
10) **before** — 'before' makes the most sense in this sentence.
11) **when** — 'when' makes the most sense in this sentence.
12) **while** — 'while' makes the most sense in this sentence.
13) **but** — 'but' makes the most sense in this sentence.
14) **because** — 'because' makes the most sense in this sentence.
15) **unless** — 'unless' makes the most sense in this sentence.
16) **whereas** — 'whereas' makes the most sense in this sentence.
17) **and** — 'and' makes the most sense in this sentence.
18) **so** — 'so' makes the most sense in this sentence.

Page 4 — Verbs

1) **the monk** — 'the monk' is the subject in this sentence because he is doing the action — 'The monk opened'.
2) **The children** — 'The children' are the subject in this sentence because they are doing the main action in the sentence — 'giggled'.
3) **viewed** — 'viewed' is the verb in this sentence because it is the action word.
4) **resigned** — 'resigned' is the verb in this sentence because it is the action word.
5) **defied** — 'defied' is the verb in this sentence because it is the action word.
6) **my family** — 'my family' is the subject in this sentence because they are doing the action — 'my family are emigrating'.
7) **Mr Evans** — 'Mr Evans' is the subject in this sentence because he is doing the action — 'Mr Evans sighed'.
8) **singing** — 'singing' is the subject in this sentence because it is doing the action — 'singing hurts'.
9) **abandoned** — 'abandoned' is the verb in this sentence because it is the action word.
10) **active** — This sentence is active because the subject (Jean) is doing the action — 'invited'.
11) **active** — This sentence is active because the subject (the solo performer) is doing the action — 'was'.
12) **active** — This sentence is active because the subject (Abdul) is doing the action — 'caught'.
13) **passive** — The verb formation 'was prevented' tells you that the sentence is passive. The sentence focuses on the action, not the subject.

14) **active** — This sentence is active because the subject (Kate) is doing the action — 'screamed'.

15) **passive** — The verb formation 'were presented' tells you that the sentence is passive. The sentence focuses on the action, not the subject.

16) **passive** — The verb formation 'will be given' tells you that the sentence is passive. The subject (I) is mentioned but the sentence focuses on the action, not the subject.

17) **passive** — The verb formation 'was flung' tells you that the sentence is passive. The sentence focuses on the action, not the subject.

18) **active** — This sentence is active because the subject (The charities) is doing the action — 'expect'.

Page 5 — Verbs

1) **sank** — The sentence should be 'When the hurricane was over, the boat sank to the sea floor.' This is the correct past tense form of the verb 'to sink' and agrees with the subject — 'boat'.

2) **was** — The sentence should be 'I was suffering last week, but I have improved since then.' This is the correct past tense form of the verb 'to be' and agrees with the subject — 'I'.

3) **Write** — The sentence should be 'Write clearly so people can comprehend what you mean.' This is an instruction so 'Write' is the only option that fits the sentence.

4) **rang** — The sentence should be 'Leo reached the door, timidly raised his hand and rang the bell.' This is the correct past tense form of the verb 'to ring' and agrees with the subject — 'Leo'.

5) **continue** — The sentence should be 'It's important that she continue to learn Spanish in the future.' This is the correct subjunctive form of the verb 'to continue'. The sentence is about the future, so you need 'continue' not 'continued'.

6) **had** — The sentence should be 'I had just finished my dinner when I heard the shrill scream.' This is the correct option to complete the verb phrase 'had just finished' — the first part of the sentence is describing something that happened in the past, so you need 'had', not 'have'.

7) **were** — The sentence should be 'If I were to win the prize, I would buy a new car.' This sentence is about a situation that isn't real, so the subjunctive 'were' is correct.

8) **forgotten** — The sentence should be 'The gerbil had forgotten where its tail was.' This is the correct option to complete the verb phrase 'had forgotten'.

9) **will** — The sentence should be 'This morning I will be going to work in a spaceship.' This sentence is about the future, so 'will' is correct.

10) **spoke** (or **was speaking**) — The sentence should be 'I spoke in class, so the teacher shouted at me.' This is the correct past tense form of the verb 'to speak'.

11) **lent** — The sentence should be 'Pedro had never lent me his favourite CD.' This is the correct option to complete the verb phrase 'had never lent'.

12) **visiting** (or **going to visit**) — The sentence should be 'Who were you visiting yesterday?' This is the correct option to complete the phrase 'were you visiting'.

13) **comes** (or **will come**) — The sentence should be 'Vivienne says she will go to the zoo if Edwina comes too.' This is the correct form of the verb 'to come'.

14) **did** (or **was doing** or **was going to do**) — The sentence should be 'Last month I did an hour of exercise every day.' This is the correct past tense form of the verb 'to do'.

15) **noticed** — The sentence should be 'We were on our way to Wales when we noticed the deflated tyre.' This is the correct past tense form of the verb 'to notice'.

16) **swam** (or **was swimming**) — The sentence should be 'When the boat capsized, the sailor swam back to shore.'

17) **threw** (or **was throwing**) — The sentence should be 'Mr Thomas threw his socks in the washing machine yesterday.' This is the correct past tense form of the verb 'to throw'.

18) **brought** (or **had brought**) — The sentence should be 'He brought crisps and lemonade to last summer's picnic.' This is the correct past tense form of the verb 'to bring'.

Page 6 — Mixed Grammar Questions

1) **their** — 'theirs' should be 'their'.

2) **was** — 'were' should be 'was'.

3) **written** — 'wrote' should be 'written'.

4) **slowly** — 'slow' should be 'slowly'.

5) **throw** — 'throws' should be 'throw'.

6) **mine** — 'my' should be 'mine'.

7) **Which** — 'What' should be 'Which'.

8) **any** — 'no' should be 'any'.

9) **are** — 'is' should be 'are'.

10) **Charlotte** — 'Charlotte' is the proper noun in this sentence.

11) **warmer** — 'warmer' is the adjective in this sentence.

12) **her** — 'her' is the pronoun in this sentence.

13) **regretfully** — 'regretfully' is the adverb in this sentence.

14) **played** — 'played' is the verb in this sentence.

15) **mouse** — 'mouse' is the common noun in this sentence.

16) **to** — 'to' is the preposition in this sentence.

17) **canary-yellow** — 'canary-yellow' is the adjective in this sentence.

18) **probably** — 'probably' is the adverb in this sentence.

Page 7 — Mixed Grammar Questions

1) **because** — The sentence should be 'I am not allowed out because I returned home late last night.'

2) **worst** — The sentence should be 'Rob was playing the worst game of rugby of his whole career.'

3) **woke** — The sentence should be 'The baby woke up early and was gurgling quietly.'

4) **despite** — The sentence should be 'Dan ran ten miles despite the very high temperature.'

5) **spoken** — The sentence should be 'She had spoken to them about road safety.'

6) **ours** — The sentence should be 'We told him that the football stickers were ours.'

7) **like** — The sentence should be 'Greta and her cousin like to go cycling in all conditions.'

8) **shook** — The sentence should be 'As he shook the groundsheet, a tiny spider sprang out.'

9) **Although** — The sentence should be 'Although the man was in agony, he limped to the hospital.'

10) **cut** — The sentence should be 'Raj cut his glossy, curly hair when his mother was distracted.'

11) **carefully** — The sentence should be 'There is a warning for all drivers to drive carefully.'

12) **which** — The sentence should be 'I discovered the pencil which I had mislaid.'

13) **went** — The sentence should be 'I would like to introduce you to my friend who went to Norway'.

14) **When** — The sentence should be 'When the puppy could not go outside, it became quite lethargic.'

15) **easily** — The sentence should be 'Davinda did not admit that she solved all of the equations easily.'

16) **had** — The sentence should be 'Angus realised that he had broken his mother's priceless vase.'

17) **took** — The sentence should be 'The polar bear took an indirect route yesterday.'

18) **whereas** — The sentence should be 'I enjoy eating trifle whereas Rebecca likes apple pie.'

Page 8 — Commas and Brackets

1) **(Member of Parliament)** — The sentence should be 'The M.P. (Member of Parliament) gave a rousing speech.' The brackets contain an explanation.

2) **(especially carrots).** — The sentence should be 'I despise vegetables (especially carrots).' The brackets contain extra information.

3) **(Friday).** — The sentence should be 'I'm catching a long-haul flight this evening (Friday).' The brackets contain extra information.

4) **(7-11 years).** — The sentence should be 'It costs £185 per child (7-11 years).' The brackets contain extra information.

5) **(a verb)** — The sentence should be 'Sprint (a verb) means to run quickly.' The brackets contain an explanation.

6) **(my tutor)** — The sentence should be 'I saw Miss Chaudhary (my tutor) shopping today.' The brackets contain an explanation.

7) **(bright red)** — The sentence should be 'Our vehicle is red (bright red) with a turquoise stripe.' The brackets contain extra information.

8) **(buns filled with cream)** — The sentence should be 'Eclairs (buns filled with cream) are mouth-watering treats.' The brackets contain an explanation.

9) **(which belong to class 4)** — The sentence should be 'The pencils (which belong to class 4) have been lost.' The brackets contain extra information.

10) **anticipation, she** — The sentence should be 'Trembling with anticipation, she opened the door.' The comma separates two clauses.

11) **hesitated, glared** — The sentence should be 'The fox hesitated, glared and sauntered away.' The comma separates a list of verbs.

12) **46, witnessed** — The sentence should be 'Mrs Jones, 46, witnessed the dangerous incident.' The pair of commas contain extra information.

13) **Maidstone, Kent.** — The sentence should be 'I sold my holiday cottage and moved to Maidstone, Kent.' The comma separates the town from the county.

14) **panda, just** — The sentence should be 'The panda, just 3 months old, was absolutely adorable.' The pair of commas contain extra information.

15) **Evania, Aunt** — The sentence should be 'Evania, Aunt Kirsty and Gita are intrepid mountaineers.' The comma separates a list of proper nouns.

16) **leaving, the** — The sentence should be 'Before leaving, the bandits, fearsome and imposing, put on their masks.' The comma separates the adverbial at the start of the sentence and clarifies the meaning of the sentence.

17) **friend, played** — The sentence should be 'The goalkeeper, my best friend, played superbly.' The comma separates the extra information and helps to clarify the meaning of the sentence.

18) **inspired, start** — The sentence should be 'So, if you feel inspired, start writing your own blog.' The pair of commas contain extra information.

Page 9 — Dashes and Hyphens

1) **use — the**
The sentence should be 'It was no use — the lock wouldn't open without the correct key.' The dash joins the two related main clauses.

2) **acrobats — the most popular act at the circus — didn't**
The sentence should be 'The acrobats — the most popular act at the circus — didn't perform last night.' The dashes separate the extra information.

3) **manager — Betsey — walking**
The sentence should be 'She saw the manager — Betsey — walking to the carpark.' The dashes separate the extra information.

4) **deserted — there**
The sentence should be 'The town was deserted — there was nobody in sight.' The dash joins the two related main clauses.

5) **carrot — they**
The sentence should be 'Flopsy gobbled up the pieces of carrot — they were delicious.' The dash joins the two related main clauses.

6) **waterfall — which was 200m high — we**
The sentence should be 'To reach the tallest waterfall — which was 200m high — we walked for hours.' The dashes separate the extra information.

7) **home — there**
The sentence should be 'I went straight home — there was nothing I could do to help.' The dash joins the two related main clauses.

8) **brother — who had always loved art — painted**
The sentence should be 'My eldest brother — who had always loved art — painted me a picture.' The dashes separate the extra information.

9) **go — he**
The sentence should be 'I didn't know where to go — he wouldn't tell me.' The dash joins the two related main clauses.

10) **correct** — The hyphen makes it clear that the legs of the bird are long.

11) **incorrect** — The sentence should be 'I found a half-eaten apple under the table'. The hyphen in the correct version of the sentence makes it clear that half of the apple has been eaten.

12) incorrect — The sentence should be 'The teacher took the seven-year-old children to the library.' The hyphens in the correct version of the sentence make it clear that all of the children in the group are aged seven.

13) correct — The hyphens make it clear that the person is questioning whether the model is the latest version.

14) incorrect — The sentence should be 'It was midnight before the wind and heavy rain stopped.' The adjectives 'wind' and 'heavy' both relate directly to the rain, so a hyphen isn't needed.

15) incorrect — The sentence should be 'The dog stole the plate of warm, fresh cookies.' The original sentence is incorrect because the hyphen makes the adjective 'warm' describe the adjective 'fresh'. As 'warm' and 'fresh' both relate directly to the cookies, a hyphen isn't needed.

16) correct — The hyphen makes it clear that the event will be a month in length.

17) incorrect — The sentence should be 'There were twelve sky-high trees in the palace gardens'. The hyphen in the correct version of the sentence makes it clear that there are twelve trees that are as high as the sky.

18) incorrect — You shouldn't use a hyphen to join two related main clauses. A dash, semicolon or full stop is needed in this sentence, e.g. 'I won't go — you should carry on without me.'

Page 10 — Apostrophes

1) **wasn't** — 'wasn't' is a shortened version of 'was not' — the apostrophe represents the missing letters.

2) **tiger's** — The possessive apostrophe goes before the 's' because there is only one tiger.

3) **she'll** — 'she'll' is a shortened version of 'she will' — the apostrophe represents the missing letters.

4) **Mr Smith's** — The possessive apostrophe goes before the 's' because there is only one Mr Smith.

5) **We'd** — 'We'd' is a shortened version of 'We would' — the apostrophe represents the missing letters.

6) **babies'** — The possessive apostrophe goes at the end of the word because 'babies' is plural and ends in 's'.

7) **We're** — 'We're' is a shortened version of 'We are' — the apostrophe represents the missing letters.

8) **women's** — The possessive apostrophe goes before the 's' because 'women' is a plural noun. The 's' shows possession — it doesn't make the noun plural.

9) **bike's** — The possessive apostrophe goes before the 's' because there is only one bike.

10) **It's** — 'It's' is a shortened version of 'it is' so it needs an apostrophe.

11) **its** — 'its' is possessive so it doesn't need an apostrophe. It shows that the paw belongs to the dog.

12) **It's** — 'It's' is a shortened version of 'It has' so it needs an apostrophe.

13) **it's** — 'it's' is a shortened version of 'it is' so it needs an apostrophe.

14) **its** — 'its' is possessive so it doesn't need an apostrophe. It shows that the cuisine belongs to Italy.

15) **it's** — 'it's' is a shortened version of 'it is' so it needs an apostrophe.

16) **its** — 'its' is possessive so it doesn't need an apostrophe. It shows that the lights belong to the car.

17) **it's** — 'it's' is a shortened version of 'it is' so it needs an apostrophe.

18) **its** — 'it's' is possessive so it doesn't need an apostrophe. It shows that the doors belong to the shop.

Page 11 — Inverted Commas, Colons and Semicolons

1) **"The toffees were delicious," she said.**
Make sure you add a comma before the second set of inverted commas. Other variations are correct.

2) **"I was on time last night," Pasua claimed.**
Make sure you change 'she' to 'I' because Pasua is talking about herself. Other variations are correct.

3) **"Could I be excused?" he asked politely.**
Make sure you add a question mark before the second set of inverted commas. Other variations are correct.

4) **"It wasn't my fault," Carlos explained.**
Make sure you change 'his' to 'my' because Carlos is talking about himself. Other variations are correct.

5) **"I started the fire," he admitted.**
Make sure you add a comma before the second set of inverted commas. Other variations are correct.

6) **bring: a towel**
The sentence should be 'There are some items you need to bring: a towel, sunglasses and some goggles.' This colon introduces a list.

7) **fists; sweets**
The sentence should be 'The shop sold mints as big as fists; sweets that fizzed; and dark liquorice balls.' The semicolons are used to separate phrases in a list.

8) **happen: he**
The sentence should be 'Roberto knew what was about to happen: he was going to be sick.' This colon introduces an explanation.

9) **off; Liang**
The sentence should be 'The referee sent the footballer off; Liang visibly winced as he passed.' This semicolon joins two main clauses to make one sentence.

10) **countries: Turkey**
The sentence should be 'Julie had visited several countries: Turkey, Thailand and Brazil.' This colon introduces a list.

11) **nightmares; I don't**
The sentence should be 'Cheese gives me nightmares; I don't eat it before bedtime.' This semicolon joins two main clauses to make one sentence.

12) **thing: her**
The sentence should be 'The girl was motivated by one thing: her love of money.' This colon introduces an explanation.

13) **alphabet: a,**
The sentence should be 'There are five vowels in the alphabet: a, e, i, o and u.' This colon introduces a list.

14) **interesting; she**
The sentence should be 'Fiona's book was very interesting; she couldn't stop reading it.' This semicolon joins two main clauses to make one sentence.

Page 12 — Mixed Punctuation Questions

1) **its** — 'it's' should be 'its' — it shows possession.

2) **Spain** — 'spain' should be 'Spain' — it is a proper noun.

3) **the** — 'The' should be 'the' — it is in the middle of a sentence.

4) **wants** — 'want's' should be 'wants' — it isn't a shortened version of a word.

5) **men's** — 'mens' should be 'men's' — the noun is already plural so the 's' at the end shows that a possessive apostrophe is needed.

6) **men** — 'Men' should be 'men' — it is not a proper noun.

7) **couldn't** — 'could'nt' should be 'couldn't' — the apostrophe shows where the words have been shortened and the 'o' is missing.

8) **eggs** — 'Eggs' should be 'eggs' — you don't need a capital letter after a colon.

9) **Yosef's** — 'Yosefs' should be 'Yosef's' — you need a possessive apostrophe because the birthday party belongs to 'Yosef'.

10) "Don't pop the balloon!" Melissa shouted frantically.
There should be a second set of inverted commas after the exclamation mark — inverted commas always come in pairs.

11) "Have those bikes been abandoned?" asked the policeman.
The policeman is asking a question so there should be a question mark before the second set of inverted commas.

12) The sun, which was nearly setting, shone in the driver's eyes.
There should be a comma between 'setting' and 'shone' to separate the extra information — 'which was nearly setting'.

13) Skateboarding is something that children (and some adults) are good at.
There should be an opening bracket between 'children' and 'and' — brackets always come in pairs.

14) "Make sure your experiment is precise," the professor instructed.
There should be a comma after 'precise' inside the inverted commas.

15) Mario smiled with satisfaction: the room was spotlessly clean.
There should be a colon between 'satisfaction' and 'the' — the colon introduces an explanation.

16) You need three items of stationery: a pen, a pencil case and a notepad.
There should be a colon between 'stationery' and 'a pen' — the colon introduces a list.

17) The latest fashions, in a variety of styles and sizes, are on sale now.
There should be a comma between 'fashions' and 'in' to separate the extra information — 'in a variety of styles and sizes'.

18) The lorries' number plates were covered in grime and dust.
There should be an apostrophe at the end of the word 'lorries' because the noun is plural and the apostrophe shows possession.

Page 13 — Mixed Punctuation Questions

1) **Buster was beaming at him and, although he was angry, the boy found himself reluctant to shout at the puppy with his glossy fur, wet little nose and floppy ears. "You are so troublesome," he muttered.**
The bits that are underlined show where punctuation has been added. You get one mark for each of the following: a capital letter at the start of 'Buster'; a comma between 'and' and 'although'; a comma between 'angry' and 'the'; a comma between 'fur' and 'wet'; a full stop after 'ears'; opening inverted commas before 'You'; a capital letter at the beginning of 'You'; a comma after 'troublesome'; closing inverted commas after this comma; a full stop after 'muttered'.

2) **Buttons, played by Joe Greco, was the star of the pantomime. All the critics agreed that the scenery and lighting could not have been better. What a success!**
The bits that are underlined show where punctuation has been added. You get one mark for each of the following: a capital letter at the start of 'Buttons'; a comma between 'Buttons' and 'played'; a capital letter at the start of 'Joe'; a capital letter at the start of 'Greco'; a comma after 'Greco'; a full stop after 'pantomime'; a capital letter at the start of 'All'; a full stop after 'better'; a capital letter at the start of 'What'; an exclamation mark (or full stop) after 'success'.

3) **My birthday party is being held at Carnwick Village Hall. There's going to be a clown and a chocolate gateau. It will be the best ever.**
The bits that are underlined show where punctuation has been added. You get one mark for each of the following: a capital letter at the start of 'My'; a capital letter at the start of 'Carnwick'; a capital letter at the start of 'Village'; a capital letter at the start of 'Hall'; a full stop after 'Hall'; a capital letter at the start of 'There's'; an apostrophe in 'There's'; a full stop after 'gateau'; a capital letter at the start of 'It'; a full stop or an exclamation mark after 'ever'.

Page 14 — Plurals

1) volcanoes
'volcano' becomes 'volcanoes' — some words ending in 'o' add 'es' to make the plural.

2) wolves
'wolf' becomes 'wolves' — often words ending in 'f' lose the final 'f' and add 'ves' to make the plural.

3) chiefs
'chief' becomes 'chiefs' — this is different to most words ending in 'f' because only 's' is added to make the plural.

4) libraries
'library' becomes 'libraries' — when the letter before the 'y' is a consonant, 'ies' is added to make the plural.

5) pianos
'piano' becomes 'pianos' — some words ending in 'o' add 's' to make the plural.

6) tomatoes
'tomato' becomes 'tomatoes' — some words ending in 'o' add 'es' to make the plural.

7) thieves
'thief' becomes 'thieves' — often words ending in 'f' lose the final 'f' and add 'ves' to make the plural.

8) elves
'elf' becomes 'elves' — often words ending in 'f' lose the final 'f' and add 'ves' to make the plural.

9) roofs
'roof' becomes 'roofs' — this is different to most words ending in 'f' because only 's' is added to make the plural.

10) oases
'oasis' becomes 'oases' — this is an irregular plural.

11) fungi
'fungus' becomes either 'funguses' or 'fungi' — this can be both a regular and an irregular plural.

12) these
'this' becomes 'these' — this is an irregular plural.

13) dice
'die' becomes 'dice' — this is an irregular plural.

14) deer
'deer' does not change — this is an irregular plural.

15) women
'woman' becomes 'women' — this is an irregular plural.

16) crises
'crisis' becomes 'crises' — this is an irregular plural.

17) those
'that' becomes 'those' — this is an irregular plural.

18) moose
'moose' does not change — this is an irregular plural.

Page 15 — Homophones

1) herd
'herd' makes sense here — it is the word for a group of cows, whereas 'heard' means 'listened to'.

2) whether
'whether' makes sense here — it is a word used to express a choice between two things, whereas 'weather' means 'day to day climate'.

3) cereal
'cereal' makes sense here — it is something you eat for breakfast, whereas 'serial' means a 'part of a series'.

4) muscles
'muscles' makes sense here — it is the part of the body that controls movement, whereas 'mussels' are a type of seafood.

5) sauce
'sauce' makes sense here — it is the word for a liquid you pour over food, whereas 'source' means 'a place where something comes from'.

6) past
'past' makes sense here — it is a preposition showing where the truck drove, whereas 'passed' is a verb meaning 'to move in relation to other things'.

7) vane
'vane' makes sense here — it is an object that shows wind direction, whereas 'vain' means 'having a high opinion of yourself'.

8) sole
'sole' makes sense here — it is the bottom of a shoe, whereas 'soul' means 'the spiritual part of a person'.

9) reigned
'reigned' makes sense here — it means 'to rule over', whereas 'reined' means 'to cause something to stop or change direction'.

10) there
'there' makes sense here — it is a word used to refer to a particular place, whereas 'they're' is a shortened version of 'they are' and 'their' means 'belonging to them'.

11) too
'too' makes sense here — it is a word used to emphasise something, whereas 'to' shows direction and 'two' is a number.

12) buy
'buy' makes sense here — it means 'to purchase', whereas 'by' is a preposition used to identify who or what is doing something and 'bye' is a shortened form of 'goodbye'.

13) where
'where' makes sense here — it is a word that refers to a location, whereas 'wear' means 'to put something on your body', and 'ware' is a word for a type of pottery.

14) right
'right' makes sense here — it means 'correct', whereas 'rite' means 'a religious act' and 'write' means 'to put letters on paper'.

15) awe
'awe' makes sense here — 'in awe' means 'impressed', whereas 'ore' is a type of mineral and 'oar' is another word for 'a paddle'.

16) pause
'pause' makes sense here — it means 'a temporary break or gap', whereas 'pours' means 'to dispense liquid' and 'paws' means 'an animal's feet'.

17) Buy
'Buy' makes sense here — it means 'to purchase', whereas 'by' is a preposition used to identify who or what is doing something and 'bye' is a shortened form of 'goodbye'.

18) praise
'praise' makes sense here — it means 'thanks or recognition', whereas 'prays' means 'to speak to a god' and 'preys' means 'to attack something'.

Page 16 — Prefixes and Suffixes

1) **mis** — The word is 'mistaken'.
2) **un** — The word is 'uncertain'.
3) **in** — The word is 'inedible'.
4) **re** — The word is 'retrace'.
5) **dis** — The word is 'dishonest'.
6) **re** — The word is 'reviews'.
7) **in** — The word is 'incapable'.
8) **dis** — The word is 'disagreement'.
9) **pre** — The word is 'preheat'.
10) **musician** — The suffix added is 'ian'.
11) **tidiness** — The suffix added is 'ness', but you also need to change the 'y' in 'tidy' to an 'i' — this is quite common for words ending in 'y'.
12) **childhood** — The suffix added is 'hood'.
13) **argument** — The suffix added is 'ment', but you also need to remove the 'e' from 'argue'.
14) **education** — The suffix added is 'ion', but you also need to remove the 'e' from 'educate'.
15) **hopeful** — The suffix added is 'ful'.
16) **imaginary** — The suffix added is 'ary', but you also need to remove the 'e' from 'imagine'.
17) **valuable** — The suffix added is 'able', but you also need to remove the 'e' from 'value'.
18) **courageous** — The suffix added is 'ous'.

Page 17 — Awkward Spellings

1) **ei** — The word is 'receive'. It follows this rule: 'i before e except after c, but only when it rhymes with bee'.
2) **ei** — The word is 'ceiling'. It follows this rule: 'i before e except after c, but only when it rhymes with bee'.
3) **ei** — The word is 'deceived'. It follows this rule: 'i before e except after c, but only when it rhymes with bee'.
4) **ei** — The word is 'weird'. It is an exception to this rule: 'i before e except after c, but only when it rhymes with bee'.
5) **ie** — The word is 'shield'. It follows this rule: 'i before e except after c, but only when it rhymes with bee'.
6) **ei** — The word is 'perceive'. It follows this rule: 'i before e except after c, but only when it rhymes with bee'.
7) **ie** — The word is 'medieval'. It follows this rule: 'i before e except after c, but only when it rhymes with bee'.
8) **ei** — The word is 'leisure'. It follows this rule: 'i before e except after c, but only when it rhymes with bee' and 'leisure' doesn't rhyme with 'bee'.
9) **ei** — The word is 'seized'. This is an exception to the 'i before e' rule.
10) **mb sc** — The sentence is 'Mina caught her thumb in the blades of the scissors.'
11) **pp kn** — The sentence is 'The chef chopped the cabbage with a sharp knife.'
12) **ff pp** — The sentence is 'The kitten's fur, which used to be fluffy, was dripping wet.'

13) kn tt — The sentence is 'Grandma was busy knitting a jumper for her little grandson.'

14) mm gn — The sentence is 'The hotel's accommodation was very expensive, so they ignored the vacancy sign.'

15) wr mm — The sentence is 'Jimmy asked his mother if she would write a note to excuse him from going swimming.'

16) dd kn — The sentence is 'When he jumped into the puddle, the water came up to his knees!'

17) pp bb — The sentence is 'The rabbit's floppy ears dangled as he nibbled on a carrot.'

18) kn sw — The sentence is 'The dashing knight picked up his helmet and sword before the battle'.

Page 18 — Mixed Spelling Questions

1) **extremely** — 'extreamly' should be 'extremely' — the root word is 'extreme'.
2) **embarrassed** — 'embarassed' should be 'embarrassed' — the root word is 'embarrass'.
3) **fourth** — 'forth' should be 'fourth' — the 'u' is not removed from the root word 'four', as it is in the word 'forty'.
4) **distance** — 'distence' should be 'distance' — it ends in 'ance'.
5) **definitely** — 'definately' should be 'definitely' — the root word is 'definite'.
6) **disgusting** — 'discusting' should be 'disgusting' — the root word is 'disgust'.
7) **disguise** — 'disgise' should be 'disguise' — if the word has a 'g', there is often a 'u' between the 'g' and the next vowel, like the word 'guess'.
8) **convince** — 'convinse' should be 'convince' — it ends in 'ce'.
9) **stomach** — 'stomack' should be 'stomach' — it ends with 'ch'.
10) **immediate** — 'imediate' should be 'immediate' — it has a double 'm'.
11) **deafened** — 'deafend' should be 'deafened' — it ends in 'ed' because it is the past tense form of the verb 'to deafen'.
12) **hesitantly** — 'hesitently' should be 'hesitantly' — the root word is 'hesitant'.
13) **private** — 'privite' should be 'private' — it ends in 'ate'.
14) **selection** — 'seleccion' should be 'selection' — the root word is 'select'.
15) **desperate** — 'desparate' should be 'desperate' — it should have 'per' in the middle.
16) **receipt** — 'reciept' should be 'receipt' — it has 'ei' in the middle because it follows the 'i before e except after c' rule.
17) **dessert** — 'desert' should be 'dessert' — it has a double 's' in the middle when it means 'pudding' or 'sweet course'.
18) **guaranteed** — 'garanteed' should be 'guaranteed' — the root word is 'guarantee' and there is often a 'u' between the 'g' and the next vowel when the word contains a 'g'.

Page 19 — Mixed Spelling Questions

1) **practise** — 'practise' makes sense here because it is a verb in the sentence.
2) **practice** — 'practice' makes sense here because it is a noun in the sentence.
3) **effect** — 'effect' makes sense here because it is a noun in the sentence.
4) **affect** — 'affect' makes sense here because it is a verb in the sentence.
5) **principal** — 'principal' makes sense here because it means 'a head teacher'.
6) **principle** — 'principle' makes sense here because it means 'a rule or belief'.
7) **fewer** — 'fewer' makes sense here because 'ducks' is a plural noun.
8) **less** — 'less' makes sense here because 'money' is not a plural noun.
9) **brought** — 'brought' makes sense here because it is the past tense of 'to bring'.
10) **bought** — 'bought' makes sense here because it is the past tense of 'to buy'.
11) **passed** — 'passed' makes sense here because it means 'completed something successfully'.
12) **past** — 'past' makes sense here because it means 'something that happened previously'.
13) **advice** — 'advice' makes sense here because it is a noun in this sentence.
14) **advise** — 'advise' makes sense here because it is a verb in this sentence.
15) **accept** — 'accept' makes sense here because it means 'to take'.
16) **except** — 'except' makes sense here because it means 'not including'.
17) **devise** — 'devise' makes sense here because it is the verb in the sentence.
18) **device** — 'device' makes sense here because it is a noun in the sentence.

Page 20 — Alliteration and Onomatopoeia

1) giant jumped giraffe's jaws
The 'j' sound is used to form the alliteration. 'giant' and 'giraffe' have a 'j' sound at the beginning so they are part of the alliteration. 'grasped' is not part of the alliteration because it starts with a 'g' sound.

2) fanned flames furiously fought phone firemen
The 'f' sound is used to form the alliteration. 'phone' has an 'f' sound at the beginning so it is part of the alliteration.

3) king crept curtains caused
The 'c' sound is used to form the alliteration. 'king' has a 'c' sound at the beginning so it is part of the alliteration. 'choke' is not part of the alliteration because it starts with a 'ch' sound.

4) pony pranced played prank
The 'p' sound is used to form the alliteration. 'phantom' is not part of the alliteration because it starts with a softer 'ph' sound.

5) Hannah hoped Henry home
The 'h' sound is used to form the alliteration. 'hour' is not part of the alliteration because the 'h' is silent.

6) knew nearly knocked new
The 'n' sound is used to form the alliteration. 'knocked' and 'knew' have a silent 'k' at the beginning so they are part of the alliteration.

7) Wendy watched while wacky wigs
The 'w' sound is used to form the alliteration. 'writers' is not part of the alliteration because the 'w' is silent.

8) graciously guarded grand glorious garden
The hard 'g' sound is used to form the alliteration. 'gnome' is not part of the alliteration because the 'g' is silent.

9) robber raided wrong room wrestled
The 'r' sound is used to form the alliteration. 'wrong' and 'wrestled' have a silent 'w' at the beginning so they are part of the alliteration.

10) rustle — 'rustle' sounds like the noise leaves make when they move.

11) Hissing — 'Hissing' sounds like the noise a cat makes when its angry.

12) banged — 'banged' sounds like the noise a door makes when it slams shut.

13) wheezing — 'wheezing' sounds like the noise a person makes when they have a bad cough.

14) tooted — 'tooted' sounds like the noise a car horn makes.

15) whizzed — 'whizzed' sounds like the noise a bicycle makes when it moves quickly.

16) fizzed — 'fizzed' sounds like the noise fizzy drinks make when they are poured.

17) yelped — 'yelped' sounds like the noise someone makes if they are in sudden pain.

18) crackling — 'crackling' sounds like the noise a log fire makes.

Page 21 — Imagery

1) personification — This is personification because the sun 'smiled' like a person.

2) metaphor — This is a metaphor because her heart is described as being made of ice.

3) metaphor — This is a metaphor because Jaione's grandfather is described as being an owl.

4) personification — This is personification because the newspapers 'screamed' like people.

5) simile — This is a simile because the man is being compared to an elephant.

6) metaphor — This is a metaphor because the footballer is described as being a streak of lightning.

7) personification — This is personification because the moonlight 'danced' like a person.

8) metaphor — This is a metaphor because the snow is described as being a blanket.

9) simile — This is a simile because the Christmas lights are being compared to diamonds.

10) many answers possible — e.g. 'sauna' or 'furnace'.

11) many answers possible — e.g. 'tomato' or 'post box'.

12) many answers possible — e.g. 'swan' or 'fairy'.

13) many answers possible — e.g. 'foghorn' or 'storm'.

14) many answers possible — e.g. 'cheetah' or 'leopard'.

15) many answers possible — e.g. 'gold' or 'diamonds'.

16) many answers possible — e.g. 'bullet' or 'tiger'.

17) many answers possible — e.g. 'night' or 'a black hole'.

18) many answers possible — e.g. 'skyscraper' or 'mountain'.

Page 22 — Abbreviations

1) approximately — 'approx' is an abbreviation for 'approximately'.

2) Department — 'Dept' is an abbreviation for 'Department'.

3) centimetres — 'cm' is an abbreviation for 'centimetres'.

4) pence — 'p' is an abbreviation for 'pence'.

5) versus — 'v' is an abbreviation for 'versus'.

6) Avenue — 'Ave' is an abbreviation for 'Avenue'.

7) Professor — 'Prof' is an abbreviation for 'Professor'.

8) Mount — 'Mt' is an abbreviation for 'Mount'.

9) ounces — 'oz' is an abbreviation for 'ounces'.

10) abbreviated word — 'Ltd' is an abbreviation for 'Limited'.

11) acronym — 'NASA' is the acronym for 'National Aeronautics and Space Administration'.

12) abbreviated word — 'Utd' is an abbreviation for 'United'.

13) abbreviated word — 'Jr' is an abbreviation for 'Junior'.

14) abbreviated word — 'max' is an abbreviation for 'maximum'.

15) acronym — 'FIFA' is the acronym for 'Fédération Internationale de Football Association'.

16) abbreviated word — 'Co' is an abbreviation for 'Company'.

17) abbreviated word — 'Aug' is an abbreviation for 'August'.

18) acronym — 'NATO' is the acronym for 'North Atlantic Treaty Organisation'.

Page 23 — Synonyms and Antonyms

1) derelict — 'ruined' and 'derelict' both mean 'damaged' or 'neglected'.

2) anxious — 'apprehensive' and 'anxious' both mean 'nervous'.

3) consoled — 'comforted' and 'consoled' both mean 'to give comfort to someone'.

4) blamed — 'scolded' and 'blamed' both mean 'to be told off'.

5) entertaining — 'amusing' and 'entertaining' both mean 'humorous'.

6) revolve — 'rotate' and 'revolve' both mean 'turn in circles'.

7) daunted — 'intimidated' and 'daunted' both mean 'to feel frightened or nervous'.

8) dangerous — 'hazardous' and 'dangerous' both mean 'unsafe'.

9) pursued — 'chased' and 'pursued' both mean 'to go closely behind'.

10) relished — 'loathed' means 'hated', whereas 'relished' means 'enjoyed'.

11) clear — 'bewildering' means 'confusing', whereas 'clear' means 'easy to understand'.

12) rapid — 'sluggish' means 'slow', whereas 'rapid' means 'fast'.

13) ignorant — 'aware' means 'to know', whereas 'ignorant' means 'to not know'.

14) helped — 'hindered' means 'to get in the way of something', whereas 'helped' means 'to assist with something'.

15) unsure — 'confident' means 'certain', whereas 'unsure' means 'uncertain'.

16) impressed — 'appalled' means 'dismayed or horrified', whereas 'impressed' means 'pleased'.

17) exposed — 'sheltered' means 'protected', whereas 'exposed' means 'unprotected'.

18) insincere — 'genuine' means 'authentic', whereas 'insincere' means 'false'.

Page 24 — Spotting and Understanding Devices

1) **alliteration** — The 'd' sound is repeated at the beginning of 'dreary', 'drops', 'drizzled' and 'down'.
2) **onomatopoeia** — 'splashed' sounds like the noise water makes when it moves.
3) **metaphor** — This is a metaphor because it is describing his smile as being sunlight.
4) **simile** — This is a simile because Wenona is compared to an elf.
5) **sci-fi** — 'sci-fi' is an abbreviation for 'science fiction'.
6) **a huge lorry screamed past** — 'a huge lorry screamed past' is personification because the lorry is being described like a person.
7) **dreary** — 'dreary' and 'bleak' both mean 'dull or dismal'.
8) **drenched** — 'drenched' means 'covered in water', whereas 'dry' means 'not covered in water'.
9) **slender** — 'broad' means 'wide', whereas 'slender' means 'thin'.
10) **quickly** — 'quickly' and 'rapidly' both mean 'fast'.

Page 25 — Spotting and Understanding Devices

1) **A** — The word 'muttered' gives the impression that the soldier is annoyed.
2) **B** — This comparison tells you that the grappling hook moves quickly because rockets move very quickly.
3) **C** — 'Clanged' is onomatopoeic so it helps you imagine the noise.
4) **A** — The image of a dagger is frightening so it makes the speaker sound dangerous.
5) **A** — The man is exaggerating because the wall cannot be 10 miles high.
6) **C** — The man is being ironic because there are 'a few hundred guards' (line 5) so to overpower them would not be easy.

Page 26 — Writing Fiction

There are many possible answers to the questions on this page. We've put some ideas below to help.

1) **e.g.** 'horrible', 'wicked' or 'dishonest'.
2) **e.g.** 'bitter', 'frozen' or 'biting'.
3) **e.g.** 'terrifying', 'petrifying' or 'hair-raising'.
4) **e.g.** 'stunning', 'breathtaking' or 'beautiful'.
5) **e.g.** 'livid', 'furious' or 'irate'.
6) **e.g.** 'pleasant', 'wonderful' or 'marvellous'.
7) **e.g.** 'unusual', 'bizarre' or 'weird'.
8) **e.g.** 'fantastic', 'astounding' or 'astonishing'.
9) **e.g.** 'loud', 'rowdy' or 'deafening'.
10) **e.g.** 'Muniza went to school, although she wasn't very well.'
11) **e.g.** 'Tia ate her dinner, but secretly gave her brussels sprouts to the dog.'
12) **e.g.** 'Mr Greg smiled when he thought about their holiday to Cornwall.'
13) **e.g.** 'He jumped into the pool and caused a tidal wave.'
14) **e.g.** 'Franziska looked at her bike as it lay in the muddy ditch.'
15) **e.g.** 'The boy cried after he lost his pet octopus.'
16) **e.g.** 'The netball team lost, even though they had trained hard.'
17) **e.g.** 'Fiona listened to the singing which reminded her of her last visit to the cathedral.'
18) **e.g.** 'He walked over the bridge but he knew he would return to claim his prize one day.'

Page 27 — Writing Fiction

There are many possible answers to the questions on this page. We've put some ideas below to help.

1) **e.g.** 'leathery', 'colossal' or 'fiery'.
2) **e.g.** 'barren', 'rocky' or 'abandoned'.
3) **e.g.** 'reckless', 'daring' or 'unexpected'.
4) **e.g.** 'narrow', 'endless' or 'pitch-black'.
5) **e.g.** 'sprightly', 'cunning' or 'brave'.
6) **e.g.** 'haunted', 'moonlit' or 'eerie'.
7) **e.g.** 'bustling', 'tense' or 'nail-biting'.
8) **e.g.** 'joyous', 'spectacular' or 'manic'.
9) **e.g.** 'wise', 'cuddly' or 'lonely'.
10) **e.g.** 'draughty', 'quaint' or 'old-fashioned'.
11) **e.g.** 'jolly', 'adventurous' or 'lengthy'.
12) **e.g.** 'intelligent', 'proud' or 'responsible'.
13) **many answers possible** — make sure you plan the beginning, middle and end of your story and then stick to your plan when you are writing.
14) **many answers possible** — make sure you plan the beginning, middle and end of your story and then stick to your plan when you are writing.
15) **many answers possible** — make sure you plan the beginning, middle and end of your story and then stick to your plan when you are writing.
16) **many answers possible** — make sure you plan the beginning, middle and end of your story and then stick to your plan when you are writing.
17) **many answers possible** — make sure you plan the beginning, middle and end of your story and then stick to your plan when you are writing.

Page 28 — Writing Non-Fiction

1) **P** — This sentence is trying to persuade the reader to visit Yardby.
2) **D** — This sentence is describing the penguin.
3) **P** — This sentence is trying to persuade the reader to donate to 'Cats in Hats'.
4) **I** — This sentence is informing the reader about badminton.
5) **I** — This sentence is informing the reader about Mount Everest.
6) **D** — This sentence is describing a day.
7) **P** — This sentence is trying to persuade the reader not to throw litter in the garden.
8) **many answers possible**
It's important to structure your writing — writing a clear plan like this will help you write a structured answer in the test.
9) **many answers possible**
It's important to structure your writing — writing a clear plan like this will help you write a structured answer in the test.

Page 29 — Writing Non-Fiction

There are many possible answers to the questions on this page. We've put some ideas below to help.

1) **e.g.** — For: Everyone looks the same, so children won't be teased about their clothes. Against: School uniform isn't comfortable.

2) **e.g.** — For: Cycling is better for the environment. Against: Cycling is difficult over long distances.

3) **e.g.** — For: A pet is a good companion. Against: Pets are expensive to look after.

4) **e.g.** — For: You can learn things from television. Against: Watching too much television is unhealthy.

5) **e.g.** — For: If you look good, you feel good about yourself. Against: It shouldn't matter how you look, people should like you for who you are.

6) **e.g.** — Make sure you plan an introduction, at least three middle points and a conclusion, and then stick to your plan when you are writing.

7) **e.g.** — Make sure you plan an introduction, at least three middle points and a conclusion, and then stick to your plan when you are writing.

8) **e.g.** — Make sure you plan an introduction, at least three middle points and a conclusion, and then stick to your plan when you are writing.

9) **e.g.** — Make sure you plan an introduction, at least three middle points and a conclusion, and then stick to your plan when you are writing.

10) **e.g.** — Make sure you plan an introduction, at least three middle points and a conclusion, and then stick to your plan when you are writing.

Pages 30-37 — Assessment Test 1

1) **A** — Daniel is anxious about starting his new school.

2) **D** — In the passage it says that Daniel "squinted through the thick lenses of his spectacles". This shows that Daniel wears glasses.

3) **B** — In the passage Mr Graham is described as ""towering", which is another word for 'tall'.

4) **D** — Daniel says his name wrong when he speaks to Rachael because he is nervous.

5) **C** — In the passage it says "he was sure that he would be teased", so Daniel thinks the other pupils will be unkind.

6) **C** — Rachael's brother is in "the year above" which shows that he already goes to the school.

7) **E** — In the passage it says "Daniel thought secondary school might not be so bad after all." This shows that he is relieved because being at school is not as bad as he thought.

8) **C** — Daniel's dad is Mr Graham, so Daniel's surname is Graham.

9) **C** — "address" is closest in meaning to 'speech' In this context, a "welcome address" is a speech given to welcome the new pupils to the school.

10) **E** — "severe" is closest in meaning to 'strict'. The headmaster is 'strict' because he does not put up with any nonsense.

11) **E** — "simultaneously" is closest in meaning to 'at the same time'. Mr Graham will be both Daniel's father and his headmaster at the same time.

12) **A** — This is a simile because the author is saying that the corridor is like the throat of a beast.

13) **C** — A rhetorical question is one that you are not expected to answer. Rachael does not expect Daniel to answer the question.

14) **D** — This phrase means that somebody seems scary because they shout a lot, but they are not as scary as they seem. Mr Graham's words are frightening, but his actions are not.

15) **D** — In the poem it says that the brook flows by "half a hundred bridges" which is fifty.

16) **C** — In verse 2, the brook flows into a river: "I flow / To join the brimming river."

17) **A** — There is no mention of fish in the brook.

18) **E** — In verse 3, the brook flows over "stony ways" and "pebbles".

19) **B** — The river is described as "brimming" which means 'full of water'.

20) **D** — In the sixth verse, the poet mentions a "sunbeam".

21) **A** — In the fourth verse, the brook makes a 'chattering' sound which means 'to talk quickly' so the poet is comparing the brook to the sound of people talking.

22) **D** — It means people's lives are short in comparison to the brook, which will always be there.

23) **A** — "skimming" means 'to glide along a surface'.

24) **E** — "babble" is closest in meaning to 'make noise continually'. The noise of water against pebbles makes a constant sound.

25) **D** — "plots" means 'pieces of land' in this context.

26) **D** — "hurry" is a verb in this context because it is used as an 'action' word in "I hurry".

27) **A** — Chattering is something that people do, so it is personification because the river is described as 'doing' a human action.

28) **E** — 'I' is a pronoun because it is used in place of a noun, the brook.

29) **A** — 'complane' should be 'complain' — the ending is 'ain'.

30) **B** — 'begining' should be 'beginning' — when the suffix 'ing' is added, the 'n' is doubled, like 'running' and 'planning'.

31) **N** — There are no mistakes in this line.

32) **A** — 'appearence' should be 'appearance' — the suffix 'ance' is added to the root word 'appear'.

33) **C** — 'threw' should be 'through' . These words are homophones — 'through' is correct because it means 'moving along or in something'.

34) **D** — 'recieving' should be 'receiving' — you need to use the rule: 'i' before 'e', except after 'c'.

35) **A** — 'Frog' should be 'frog' — it is a common noun, not a proper noun, so it doesn't need a capital letter.

36) **B** — 'balls' does not need an apostrophe because the 's' is added to make the word plural.

37) **N** — There are no mistakes in this line.

38) **C** — There should be a colon after 'occur' because it is the start of a list.

39) **B** — There should be a semicolon after 'grow' rather than a colon because it is part of a list of phrases.

40) **A** — 'tadpoles' needs an apostrophe before the 's' to show that the tail belongs to the tadpole.

41) B — 'except' is correct . The sentence means that only the lights from the electronic toys were on.

42) E — 'out' is correct because they are moving from their hiding place.

43) D — 'behind' is correct because it is the most likely word to describe where the children were in relation to the panda.

44) A — 'they'd' is correct because it means 'they had' and the sentence is in the past tense.

45) C — 'had' is correct because the sentence is in the past tense and 'had' comes before 'listened' to complete the sentence.

46) B — 'become' is correct because the sentence is in the past tense and 'become' follows 'had' to complete the sentence.

47) C — 'couldn't' is correct because it means 'could not'.

48) C — 'were' is correct as it agrees with 'they' and is in the past tense.

49) A — 'their' is correct as the sentence refers to the eyes belonging to the children.

50) E — 'which' is correct because it is referring to the toys.

Pages 38-45 — Assessment Test 2

1) **B** — In the passage it says the pharaohs built the pyramids as "eternal resting places to safeguard their souls".

2) **C** — In the passage it says that the pyramid was "one of the first of these tombs".

3) **C** — The passage tells us that the burial chamber was hidden underground "but this did not deter the grave robbers".

4) **D** — In the passage it says the pyramids were "built on the banks of the Nile", which is a river in Egypt.

5) **E** — In the passage it says "It was the tallest building in the world for over 3,800 years".

6) **D** — In the passage it says that the Ancient Egyptians filled their tombs with "the things they would need in the afterlife".

7) **B** — In the passage it says that a person's "actions on Earth were judged" and if they were found to be "unworthy" they were punished and "could not enter the afterlife".

8) **B** — Only the first paragraph explains why the pyramids were built. The subsequent paragraphs talk about their design and how they were built.

9) **C** — "rigorously" means the same as 'thoroughly'. It means that something has been done carefully.

10) **B** — "crude" is closest in meaning to 'rough'. It means that it was not perfect.

11) **D** — "imposing" is closest in meaning to 'impressive'. It means 'grand in appearance'.

12) **D** — "Nile" is a proper noun — it is a name of a river.

13) **C** — 'was' is a verb. It is the action word of the sentence.

14) **E** — These are adverbs because they describe verbs.

15) **C** — In the passage it says that Antonio's mother "aspired to be as strong and courageous as he was" which shows that she wants to be brave.

16) **B** — In the passage it says that the "journey had been very arduous" and Antonio had "suffered from sea-sickness" which shows that he had been ill.

17) **C** — Manolo's age is not mentioned in the text.

18) **A** — Antonio's final destination is one of the big teaching hospitals in London.

19) **C** — Antonio's father would be proud because he "had always hoped" that one of his children "would follow in his footsteps" and become a doctor.

20) **C** — In the passage it says they travelled on a "small cargo ship".

21) **A** — In the passage it says that Antonio's father had "two children" — Antonio and his "younger sister, Rosa".

22) **E** — In the passage it says that Antonio "tasted salty tears" — he felt "an ache" because his mother thought he was brave, but he was crying.

23) **E** — "intensive" means that something is 'demanding or difficult'.

24) **B** — "apprehensive" is closest in meaning to 'nervous'.

25) **C** — "inkling" is closest in meaning to 'idea', because Antonio had no idea how to get to London.

26) **B** — "arduous" is an adjective because it describes the journey.

27) **D** — 'neared' is a verb. It is the action word of the sentence.

28) **A** — Metaphors describe something as being something else. This is a metaphor because Antonio's stomach is described as having knots in it.

29) **B** — 'your' is correct as the author is speaking about the environment belonging to the reader.

30) **D** — 'instead of' is correct because it means 'in place of'.

31) **B** — 'wherever' is correct because the sentence is asking the reader to reuse materials in every possible situation.

32) **A** — 'Finally' is the best choice because it is introducing the last part of the paragraph.

33) **E** — 'other' is the word that makes sense because it refers to additional objects not previously mentioned.

34) **B** — 'can' is the word that makes sense here because it is referring to what is made from new materials.

35) **C** — There should be a comma between 'eggs' and 'sugar' to separate the items in the list of ingredients.

36) **C** — The exclamation mark should be a full stop after 'cases' because the sentence does not show strong feelings.

37) **D** — There does not need to be an apostrophe in 'egg's'. The 's' has been added to make the word plural.

38) **C** — 'mixtures' should have an apostrophe because it is short for 'mixture is'.

39) **N** — There are no mistakes in this line.

40) **A** — 'cool' should be followed by a comma.

41) **D** — 'eigth' should be spelt 'eight' . The 'g' goes before the 'h' like in 'weight' and 'height'.

42) **B** — 'hole' should be 'whole'. These words are homophones — a 'hole' is something you dig whereas 'whole' means 'entire'.

43) **B** — 'accross' should be 'across' — it only needs one 'c'.

44) **B** — 'dissapeared' should be 'disappeared' — the prefix 'dis' is added to 'appeared' so the word should have one 's' and two 'p's.

45) **N** — There are no mistakes in this line.

46) **B** — 'favarite' should be 'favourite' — the unstressed vowel is spelt 'ou'.

47) **C** — 'opportunitys' should be 'opportunities' . If the letter before the 'y' is a consonant then you remove the 'y' and add 'ies' to make it plural.

48) **N** — There are no mistakes in this line.

49) **B** — 'extremeley' should be 'extremely'. You add the suffix 'ly' to the root word 'extreme' to form 'extremely'.

50) **D** — 'imediately' should be 'immediately' — the root word is 'immediate'.

Pages 46-53 — Assessment Test 3

1) **B** — In the passage it says that Bessie came into Jane's room at five o'clock, but Jane had "risen half-an-hour before her entrance".

2) **A** — In the passage it says that Bessie tried "in vain" to get Jane to have some boiled milk and bread. This means that Bessie was unsuccessful in persuading Jane to eat any breakfast.

3) **C** — In the passage it says that Jane put on her clothes "by the light of a half-moon just setting".

4) **A** — Jane says that Mrs Reed had told her that she "need not disturb her in the morning".

5) **B** — Jane says that Mrs Reed had "not been my friend; but she has been my foe". This shows that she did not like Mrs Reed.

6) **B** — The word which best describes Bessie is helpful because she helps Jane to prepare for her journey.

7) **B** — In the passage, Jane is "excited with the thoughts of a journey".

8) **D** — The passage does not mention that Mrs Reed is Jane's aunt.

9) **B** — "pressed" is closest in meaning to 'encouraged'.

10) **A** — "hardly" means the same as 'only just'.

11) **B** — Another word for "foe" is 'enemy'.

12) **C** — "narrow" is an adjective because it describes a noun (the window).

13) **C** — "children" is a common noun because it is the name for a kind of person.

14) **E** — "with", "from" and "to" are the prepositions in this sentence.

15) **A** — In the passage Cornwall's roads are described as "steep" which is the opposite of 'flat'.

16) **B** — "brooding" implies that Bodmin Moor is dark and "granite heights" are rocky outcrops.

17) **E** — A "hearty pub lunch" is the only food that is mentioned in the passage — there is no mention of delicious seafood.

18) **A** — King Arthur was said to have been born at Tintagel which is perched above "wave-battered cliffs", which shows that it is by the sea.

19) **C** — It means that there is lots of evidence of Cornwall's history.

20) **E** — "Awash with Celtic heritage" means that there is lots of evidence of Cornwall's Celtic past.

21) **E** — The passage says that there are "gently-sloping beaches" in the south and a "rugged" coastline in the north. This shows that the coastline in the north and the south is different.

22) **D** — You would find this in a travel brochure because it is persuading the reader to visit Cornwall.

23) **A** — "isolated" is closest in meaning to 'remote'.

24) **C** — In this sentence the word "meander" could most accurately be replaced by 'twist and turn'.

25) **B** — "intrepid" is closest in meaning to 'courageous'.

26) **A** — This is an example of alliteration because the 'b' sound is repeated.

27) **A** — This is an example of a metaphor because Cornwall's history is described as being a treasure trove.

28) **C** — These words are adjectives because they describe nouns.

29) **N** — There are no mistakes in this line.

30) **D** — 'sustane' should be 'sustain' — the ending should be 'ain'.

31) **D** — 'necessery ' should be 'necessary' — the ending should be 'ary'.

32) **A** — 'approximatley' should be 'approximately'. You add the suffix 'ly' to the root word 'approximate' to form 'approximately'.

33) **B** — 'breath' should be 'breathe' — there is an 'e' at the end when the word is the verb 'breathe'.

34) **A** — 'temprature' should be 'temperature' — there should be an 'e' between the 'p' and the first 'r'.

35) **C** — 'tomorrow' is correct because the sentence is written about a future event.

36) **C** — 'in' is the correct word to describe the fair's location.

37) **D** — 'will' is the correct word to talk about the future.

38) **B** — 'from' is the word that makes most sense in this sentence.

39) **D** — 'out' is the correct word. It completes the phrase 'look out for'.

40) **B** — 'won' is the correct past tense form of 'to win'.

41) **A** — 'resident's' should be 'residents'. It does not need an apostrophe because the 's' is added to make the word plural.

42) **N** — There are no mistakes in this line.

43) **D** — There needs to be a comma after 'Price' rather than a colon.

44) **C** — Inverted commas are needed after 'cat' because it is the end of Mr Price's speech.

45) **B** — 'bears' needs an apostrophe before the 's' because the growl belongs to the bear.

46) **N** — There are no mistakes in this line.

47) **C** — There needs to be a closing comma after 'Jones'.

48) **D** — There should not be a comma after 'tired' because there is an 'and' to separate the adjectives.

49) **N** — There are no mistakes in this line.

50) **B** — 'lets' should have an apostrophe before the 's' because it is the shortened version of two words, 'let' and 'us'.

Pages 54-61 — Assessment Test 4

1) **B** — Mi Nuong is lonely because "Her father kept her locked away at the top of the palace's tallest tower."

2) **E** — Mi Nuong sits at her window "embroidering" — this is another word for sewing.

3) **C** — In the passage it says Mi Nuong's father locks her in a tower "to keep her out of harm's way."

4) **C** — Sunlight is the only option that isn't mentioned in the passage.

5) **B** — The song makes Mi Nuong feel enthralled and wishful — the music is "captivating" and gives her a "glimmer of hope".

6) **D** — The man is fishing — he stands on a "golden fishing boat" and he has a net.

7) **C** — In the passage it says "Mi Nuong leaned out as far out as she could to try to catch sight of the singer" — she wants to get a better look at the man on the fishing boat.

8) **A** — In the passage it says "A sudden glimmer of hope lit up in her heart" and "Perhaps this man had come to release her from the tower" — she is hopeful that the man has come to rescue her.

9) **C** — "forlorn" is closest in meaning to 'miserable'. It means that Mi Nuong is unhappy.

10) **B** — The phrase "floating on air" is an idiom which means 'to be overjoyed'.

11) **B** — The phrase means that Mi Nuong thinks she is meant to marry him — "destined" means the same as 'meant'.

12) **C** — This is a simile because the author is saying that Mi Nuong is like a moth.

13) **A** — "unwary" is an adjective because it is describing a noun.

14) **B** — "glimpsed" is a verb. It is the action word in this sentence.

15) **B** — In the passage it says that "She could see nothing, in fact, but a dense darkness on either side."

16) **D** — In the passage the only thing Mrs Medlock doesn't mention is water.

17) **B** — Mary feels anxious as she doesn't know anything about the moor and she says that she does not like it.

18) **C** — In the passage Mrs Medlock describes the moor as "wild" and that nothing grows on the moor "but heather and gorse".

19) **B** — Mary can only see darkness around her, which she thinks could be the sea.

20) **E** — In the passage it says "Mary felt as if the drive would never come to an end", and she's uncertain about where they are, which means that she is disorientated.

21) **A** — The author creates an unsettling mood because the moor is described as uncertain and mysterious.

22) **D** — This is a story so it's a fiction text.

23) **E** — "presently" means the same as 'before long'.

24) **C** — "expanse" is closest in meaning to 'area'.

25) **A** — "singular" is closest in meaning to 'strange'.

26) **D** — "beneath" is a preposition because it tells you where the water is in relation to the bridge.

27) **B** — This is a metaphor because the moor is described as an ocean.

28) **C** — These words are common nouns because they are names for types of things.

29) **N** — There are no mistakes in this line.

30) **D** — 'desents' should be 'descents' — there is a silent 'c' after the first 's'.

31) **A** — 'plentyful ' should be 'plentiful' — the 'y' changes to an 'i' when the suffix 'ful' is added to the word 'plenty'.

32) **C** — 'begginners" should be 'beginners' — the root word is 'begin' so there is only one 'g'.

33) **D** — 'residant' should be 'resident' — the ending should be 'ent'.

34) **C** — 'restaraunt' should be 'restaurant' — the 'u' comes before the second 'r' and the ending is 'ant'.

35) **C** — 'Asked' should be 'asked'. This word doesn't need a capital letter because it follows speech, even though the speech is a full sentence.

36) **N** — There are no mistakes in this line.

37) **D** — There should be a full stop after 'disease', but before the inverted commas.

38) **C** — There should be a semicolon after 'huge' to separate two main clauses which are related.

39) **D** — 'it's' should be 'its' — there shouldn't be an apostrophe because 'its' shows possession in this sentence.

40) **A** — The comma should be after 'listened', not after 'thought'.

41) **B** — 'was' is the correct past tense form of the verb 'be'.

42) **C** — This is the correct tense to use to complete the clause 'it's what we were all worried we'd do'. It must be 'we'd do' to agree with 'we were all worried'.

43) **B** — 'had' is the correct past tense form of 'have', to agree with 'Mum', so the correct option is 'had to'.

44) **A** — 'worse' is correct — it is used to compare two bad situations.

45) **A** — 'were' is the correct past tense form of the verb 'be' and agrees with 'Year 7s' which is plural.

46) **D** — 'to' is correct because it completes the phrase is 'in order to'.

47) **A** — 'off' is the only preposition which makes sense here.

48) **A** — 'By lunch' is the only option which makes sense.

49) **B** — 'have forgotten' is the correct past tense form to use — 'have' agrees with 'everyone' and 'forgotten' is the correct spelling to use here.

50) **D** — This is the correct past tense form of 'write' and agrees with the singular noun, 'a word'.

Pages 62-69 — Assessment Test 5

1) **D** — The only thing that is not true about the road is that 'horses have worn it away'.

2) **E** — The poet doesn't say what the road was like.

3) **E** — Lines 7-12 focus on what the woods are like now.

4) **E** — The animals are "at ease" which shows that they are 'carefree'.

5) **B** — The poet is stating a fact in the first two lines, so his tone is matter-of-fact.

6) **D** — Trout are fish and the rings on the water show where the fish are moving.

7) **B** — The otters are indifferent to men — they rarely see them so they are not frightened by them.

8) **C** — The poet is imagining people who used to use the old road.

9) **C** — The "coppice" is a group of small trees and shrubs.

10) **E** — "broods" is closest in meaning to 'hatches eggs'.

11) **C** — "cools" is the verb because it is the action word in the sentence.

12) **E** — "underneath" is a preposition because it tells you where the road is in relation to the coppice and heath.

13) **E** — "swish" is an example of onomatopoeia — the word sounds like the noise it is describing.

14) B — "solitudes" are 'lonely places'.

15) B — This means he was not promoted, despite having "good prospects".

16) E — It is not mentioned in the passage that they had a big house.

17) B — The author repeats the phrase to emphasise how desperate for money the family are.

18) C — In the passage it says "She racked her brains, and tried this thing and the other, but could not find anything successful."

19) A — In the passage it says "The failure made deep lines come into her face".

20) A — In the passage it says "he never would be able to do anything worth doing".

21) E — The family did not speak about money but the word "haunted" implies that it is a constant worry that cannot be mentioned.

22) D — The word "superior" shows that they thought they were better than their neighbours.

23) B — "anxiety" is closest in meaning to 'worry'. It describes the way the family felt troubled by their lack of money.

24) A — In this sentence the word "discreet" could most accurately be replaced by 'tactful'. It means 'being careful to avoid embarrassment'.

25) D — "grinding" is closest in meaning to 'relentless'. It means 'continuous' or 'never stopping'.

26) C — "handsome" is an adjective because it describes a noun.

27) D — "though" is a conjunction because it joins two clauses together.

28) E — The phrase "There must be more money" is a statement.

29) D — 'multycoloured' should be 'multicoloured' — the prefix is 'multi'.

30) D — 'exsquisite' should be 'exquisite' — there's no 's' between the 'x' and the 'q'.

31) A — 'guilded' should be 'gilded' — the root word is 'gild' not 'guild'.

32) D — 'peices' should be 'pieces' — the rule is: 'i' before 'e' except after 'c'.

33) N — There are no mistakes in this line.

34) D — 'rasberry' should be 'raspberry' — there is a silent 'p' in 'raspberry'.

35) B — 'rise' is correct — it is the correct tense of the verb and agrees with 'Ali', which is singular.

36) D — 'began' is the correct past tense form of the verb 'begin'.

37) C — 'with' is the only option that makes sense here.

38) A — 'filling' is the correct form of the verb 'fill'.

39) A — 'wouldn't' is correct — it is used to agree with the first clause 'However long he stayed'.

40) A — 'for' is correct because it completes the phrase 'waited for rescue'.

41) D — 'developers' needs an apostrophe after the 's' to show that the plans belong to the developers.

42) A — 'Local' doesn't need a capital letter as it's not a proper noun.

43) N — There are no mistakes in this line.

44) D — 'our's' doesn't need the apostrophe — it's a possessive pronoun (a pronoun that stands for a noun), so it already shows possession. Other possessive pronouns are 'theirs' and 'yours'.

45) A — The full stop after 'practise' should be a comma because it's inside the inverted commas and the speech continues after 'said one young protester'.

46) A — 'elderly' doesn't need a comma after it.

47) N — There are no mistakes in this line.

48) A — There doesn't need to be inverted commas before 'They've' because Elsie is still talking.

49) A — There should be a comma after 'park' to separate the extra information in the sentence.

50) B — There shouldn't be a comma after 'ramps' because it comes before 'and' in a list.

Pages 70-77 — Assessment Test 6

1) D — In the passage it says that there have been "attacks on livestock."

2) B — The passage says that "anxious" people have reported sightings — "anxious" is closest in meaning to 'concerned'.

3) C — The passage says that the reports are often regarded as "hoaxes, mistakes or fantasies" and the article also tells us that many people believe the reports to be real. So, the only option not given as a reason is that the sightings are dreams.

4) E — The passage says that "An increasing number of people believe there are too many witnesses for the rumours to be unfounded."

5) E — The passage says "some areas produce more reports of mysterious creatures than others, leading to local legends such as Cornwall's famous Beast of Bodmin". This suggests that there have been many sightings of strange animals in Cornwall.

6) A — In the passage it says that farmers "know the countryside well".

7) C — The passage says that people "were no longer permitted to keep" big cats.

8) C — The word "rage" suggests that people feel strongly about them.

9) B — "rural" is closest in meaning to 'rustic'. It means 'in the countryside'.

10) D — "mysterious" is closest in meaning to 'inexplicable'. It means that people can't explain the cause of these sightings.

11) B — "exotic" is closest in meaning to 'foreign'. It means that big cats are not native to the United Kingdom.

12) A — "United Kingdom" is a proper noun because it is the name of a particular place. Proper nouns always begin with a capital letter.

13) A — The article is biased — it provides more evidence that the sightings are true.

14) B — "wild" is an adjective. It describes a noun.

15) E — The poet is scared of the tiger; he describes it as "fearful".

16) D — The poet does not ask when the tiger was made.

17) C — The poem suggests that the creator is brave because he asks how the tiger's creator could "dare" to make it.

18) B — A "hammer", "chain", "furnace" and "anvil" are all used by a blacksmith. Although the tiger's creator is compared to a blacksmith, there's nothing to suggest that he is a blacksmith.

19) D — The question is asking whether whoever made the tiger was happy when they saw it after it had been made.

20) E — The poet is asking whether the creator made both animals. The poet finds it difficult to understand how the same creator could make such a fierce creature as a tiger and such a gentle animal as a lamb.

21) B — The poet is addressing the tiger because he uses the word "thy" to mean 'your'.

22) E — The poet asks a series of questions about how the tiger was created, but no human could really answer them.

23) A — "immortal" is closest in meaning to 'enduring'. It means 'to exist continually'.

24) B — "twist" is closest in meaning to 'wind'. It means 'to wrap something around something else'.

25) D — "seize" is closest in meaning to 'grasp'. It means 'to hold something quickly'.

26) E — "began" is a verb — it is the 'doing' word in this sentence.

27) D — It is an example of alliteration because the 'f' sound is repeated in the words "frame" and "fearful".

28) C — It is an example of personification — the poet has given the stars human qualities because they are described as throwing spears.

29) D — 'o clock' should be written as 'o'clock'. The apostrophe shows something has been left out, in this case the full phrase is 'of the clock'.

30) N — There are no mistakes in this line.

31) A — There should be a bracket between 'teachers' and the semi colon to close the bracket in the previous line. Remember brackets come in pairs.

32) C — There should not be a comma between 'night' and 'black'. 'night' tells you more about the colour black, like 'blood red' and 'sick green', so doesn't need a comma to separate the adjectives.

33) B — 'youre' should be 'you're' — the apostrophe shows that something has been left out. The full phrase here should be 'you are'.

34) D — There should be a question mark at the end of the line because the sentence is a rhetorical question.

35) D — 'before' is the only word that makes sense here.

36) D — 'must' is correct because a cage is something that a hamster requires.

37) A — 'are' is correct — it is the correct present tense form of the verb 'be' and agrees with 'Hamsters" which is plural.

38) E — 'from' is the only word that makes sense here.

39) A — 'Finally' makes sense because it is the last point in the paragraph.

40) A — 'so' is the only option that makes sense here.

41) B — 'imagenation' should be 'imagination' — the root word is 'imagine' so the vowel after the 'g' should be 'i'.

42) C — 'distent' should be 'distant' — the ending should be 'ant'.

43) C — 'accomodation' should be 'accommodation' — the word is spelt with a double 'm'.

44) A — 'sevaral' should be 'several' — the unstressed vowel is an 'e'.

45) A — 'sugested' should be 'suggested' — the root word is 'suggest' so the word is spelt with a double 'g'.

46) B — 'secritive' should be 'secretive' — the root word is 'secret'.

47) N — There are no mistakes in this line.

48) C — 'fourty' should be 'forty' — the 'u' is removed from 'four' when the suffix 'ty' is added.

49) N — There are no mistakes on this line.

50) C — 'visably' should be 'visibly' — the root word is 'visible'.

Progress Chart

Use this chart to keep track of your scores for the Assessment Tests.

You can do each test more than once — download extra answer sheets from cgpbooks.co.uk/11plus/answer-sheets or scan the QR code on the right.

	First Go	Second Go	Third Go
Test 1	Date: Score:	Date: Score:	Date: Score:
Test 2	Date: Score:	Date: Score:	Date: Score:
Test 3	Date: Score:	Date: Score:	Date: Score:
Test 4	Date: Score:	Date: Score:	Date: Score:
Test 5	Date: Score:	Date: Score:	Date: Score:
Test 6	Date: Score:	Date: Score:	Date: Score:

Look back at your scores once you've done all the Assessment Tests.
Each test is out of 50 marks.

Work out which kind of mark you scored most often:

0-29 marks — Go back to basics and work on your question technique.

30-42 marks — You're nearly there — go back over the questions you found tricky.

43-50 marks — You're an English whizz.